# GO MATH!

## Grade 8

## Solutions Key

Cover Image Credits: ©Tom Grubbe/Flickr/Getty Images

Printed in the U.S.A.

ISBN   978-1-328-77327-2

4 5 6 7 8 9 10   1026   26 25 24 23 22 21 20 19 18

4500711771            A B C D E F G

# Table of Contents

**UNIT 1** Real Numbers, Exponents, and Scientific Notation

**Module 1**
Lesson 1.1 . . . . . . . . . . . . . . . . . . . . . 1
Lesson 1.2 . . . . . . . . . . . . . . . . . . . . . 4
Lesson 1.3 . . . . . . . . . . . . . . . . . . . . . 5

**Module 2**
Lesson 2.1 . . . . . . . . . . . . . . . . . . . . . 8
Lesson 2.2 . . . . . . . . . . . . . . . . . . . . . 10
Lesson 2.3 . . . . . . . . . . . . . . . . . . . . . 12
Lesson 2.4 . . . . . . . . . . . . . . . . . . . . . 13

**UNIT 2** Proportional and Nonproportional Relationships and Functions

**Module 3**
Lesson 3.1 . . . . . . . . . . . . . . . . . . . . . 18
Lesson 3.2 . . . . . . . . . . . . . . . . . . . . . 19
Lesson 3.3 . . . . . . . . . . . . . . . . . . . . . 21

**Module 4**
Lesson 4.1 . . . . . . . . . . . . . . . . . . . . . 23
Lesson 4.2 . . . . . . . . . . . . . . . . . . . . . 25
Lesson 4.3 . . . . . . . . . . . . . . . . . . . . . 26
Lesson 4.4 . . . . . . . . . . . . . . . . . . . . . 28

**Module 5**
Lesson 5.1 . . . . . . . . . . . . . . . . . . . . . 31
Lesson 5.2 . . . . . . . . . . . . . . . . . . . . . 32
Lesson 5.3 . . . . . . . . . . . . . . . . . . . . . 34

**Module 6**
Lesson 6.1 . . . . . . . . . . . . . . . . . . . . . 37
Lesson 6.2 . . . . . . . . . . . . . . . . . . . . . 38
Lesson 6.3 . . . . . . . . . . . . . . . . . . . . . 40
Lesson 6.4 . . . . . . . . . . . . . . . . . . . . . 41

**UNIT 3** Solving Equations and Systems of Equations

**Module 7**
Lesson 7.1. . . . . . . . . . . . . . . . . . . . . 43
Lesson 7.2. . . . . . . . . . . . . . . . . . . . . 45
Lesson 7.3. . . . . . . . . . . . . . . . . . . . . 47
Lesson 7.4. . . . . . . . . . . . . . . . . . . . . 50

**Module 8**
Lesson 8.1 . . . . . . . . . . . . . . . . . . . . . 54
Lesson 8.2 . . . . . . . . . . . . . . . . . . . . . 57
Lesson 8.3 . . . . . . . . . . . . . . . . . . . . . 62
Lesson 8.4 . . . . . . . . . . . . . . . . . . . . . 65
Lesson 8.5 . . . . . . . . . . . . . . . . . . . . . 69

**UNIT 4** Transformational Geometry

**Module 9**
Lesson 9.1 . . . . . . . . . . . . . . . . . . . . . 73
Lesson 9.2 . . . . . . . . . . . . . . . . . . . . . 75
Lesson 9.3 . . . . . . . . . . . . . . . . . . . . . 77
Lesson 9.4 . . . . . . . . . . . . . . . . . . . . . 78
Lesson 9.5 . . . . . . . . . . . . . . . . . . . . . 79

**Module 10**
Lesson 10.1 . . . . . . . . . . . . . . . . . . . . 82
Lesson 10.2 . . . . . . . . . . . . . . . . . . . . 83
Lesson 10.3 . . . . . . . . . . . . . . . . . . . . 84

# Table of Contents

**UNIT 5** Measurement Geometry

**Module 11**
Lesson 11.1 . . . . . . . . . . . . . . . . . . . . . . 87
Lesson 11.2 . . . . . . . . . . . . . . . . . . . . . . 88
Lesson 11.3 . . . . . . . . . . . . . . . . . . . . . . 90

**Module 12**
Lesson 12.1 . . . . . . . . . . . . . . . . . . . . . . 92
Lesson 12.2 . . . . . . . . . . . . . . . . . . . . . . 94
Lesson 12.3 . . . . . . . . . . . . . . . . . . . . . . 96

**Module 13**
Lesson 13.1 . . . . . . . . . . . . . . . . . . . . . . 99
Lesson 13.2 . . . . . . . . . . . . . . . . . . . . . .101
Lesson 13.3 . . . . . . . . . . . . . . . . . . . . . 103

**UNIT 6** Statistics

**Module 14**
Lesson 14.1 . . . . . . . . . . . . . . . . . . . . . 106
Lesson 14.2 . . . . . . . . . . . . . . . . . . . . . 107

**Module 15**
Lesson 15.1 . . . . . . . . . . . . . . . . . . . . . 109
Lesson 15.2 . . . . . . . . . . . . . . . . . . . . . 111

# Solutions Key

## UNIT 1 — Real Numbers, Exponents, and Scientific Notation

### MODULE 1 Real Numbers

**Are You Ready?**

1. $7 \times 7 = 49$

2. $21 \times 21 = 441$

3. $(-3) \times (-3) = 9$

4. $\frac{4}{5} \times \frac{4}{5} = \frac{16}{25}$

5. $(2.7) \times (2.7) = 7.29$

6. $\left(-\frac{1}{4}\right) \times \left(-\frac{1}{4}\right) = \frac{1}{16}$

7. $(-5.7) \times (-5.7) = 32.49$

8. $1\frac{2}{5} = \frac{5}{5} + \frac{2}{5} = \frac{7}{5}$

   $\frac{7}{5} \times \frac{7}{5} = \frac{49}{25} = 1\frac{24}{25}$ or $19.6$

9. $9^2 = 9 \times 9 = 81$

10. $2^4 = 2 \times 2 \times 2 \times 2 = 16$

11. $\left(\frac{1}{3}\right)^2 = \frac{1}{3} \times \frac{1}{3} = \frac{1}{9}$

12. $(-7)^2 = (-7) \times (-7) = 49$

13. $4^3 = 4 \times 4 \times 4 = 64$

14. $(-1)^5 = (-1) \times (-1) \times (-1) \times (-1) \times (-1) = -1$

15. $(4.5)^2 = (4.5) \times (4.5) = 20.25$

16. $10^5 = 10 \times 10 \times 10 \times 10 \times 10 = 100{,}000$

17. $3\frac{1}{3}$

   $3 + \frac{1}{3}$

   $\frac{9}{3} + \frac{1}{3}$

   $\frac{10}{3}$

18. $1\frac{5}{8}$

   $1 + \frac{5}{8}$

   $\frac{8}{8} + \frac{5}{8}$

   $\frac{13}{8}$

19. $2\frac{3}{7}$

   $2 + \frac{3}{7}$

   $\frac{14}{7} + \frac{3}{7}$

   $\frac{17}{7}$

20. $5\frac{5}{6}$

   $5 + \frac{5}{6}$

   $\frac{30}{6} + \frac{5}{6}$

   $\frac{35}{6}$

### LESSON 1.1

**Your Turn**

1.
$$
\begin{array}{r}
0.\overline{45} \\
11\overline{)5.00} \\
-44 \\
\hline
60 \\
-55 \\
\hline
5
\end{array}
$$

Because the number 5 repeats during the division process, the answer is a repeating decimal: $0.\overline{45}$.

2.
$$
\begin{array}{r}
0.125 \\
8\overline{)1.000} \\
-8 \\
\hline
20 \\
-16 \\
\hline
40 \\
-40 \\
\hline
0
\end{array}
$$
$0.125$

3. $2\frac{1}{3} = \frac{7}{3}$

$$
\begin{array}{r}
2.\overline{3} \\
3\overline{)7.0} \\
-6 \\
\hline
10 \\
-9 \\
\hline
1
\end{array}
$$

Because the number 1 repeats during the division process, the answer is a repeating decimal: $2.\overline{3}$.

4. Write the decimal 0.12 as a fraction.

   $0.12 = \frac{12}{100}$

   Simplify using the same numerator and denominator.

   $\frac{12 \div 4}{100 \div 4} = \frac{3}{25}$

5. 

$$x = 0.\overline{57}$$
$$(100)x = 100(0.\overline{57})$$
$$100x = 57.\overline{57}$$

Because $x = 0.\overline{57}$, subtract $x$ from one side and $0.\overline{57}$ from the other.

$$100x = 57.\overline{57}$$
$$\underline{-x \quad\quad -0.\overline{57}}$$
$$99x = 57$$

$$\frac{99x}{99} = \frac{57}{99}$$

$$x = \frac{57}{99}, \text{ or } \frac{19}{33}$$

6. Write the decimal 1.4 as a fraction.

$$1.4 = \frac{14}{10}$$

Simplify using the same numerator and denominator.

$$\frac{14 \div 2}{10 \div 2} = \frac{7}{5}$$

$$\frac{7}{5}, \text{ or } 1\frac{2}{5}$$

7. 
$$x^2 = 196$$
$$\sqrt{x^2} = \sqrt{196}$$
$$X = \sqrt{196}$$
$$X = \pm 14$$

The solutions are 14 and −14.

8. 
$$x^2 = \frac{9}{256}$$
$$\sqrt{x^2} = \sqrt{\frac{9}{256}}$$
$$x = \sqrt{\frac{9}{256}}$$
$$x = \frac{3}{16}$$

The solutions are $\frac{3}{16}$ and $-\frac{3}{16}$.

9. 
$$512 = x^3$$
$$\sqrt[3]{512} = \sqrt[3]{x^3}$$
$$\sqrt[3]{512} = x$$
$$8 = x$$

The solution is 8.

10. 
$$x^3 = \frac{64}{343}$$
$$\sqrt[3]{x^3} = \sqrt[3]{\frac{64}{343}}$$
$$x = \frac{4}{7}$$

The solution is $\frac{4}{7}$.

**Guided Practice**

1. $\frac{2}{5}$

$$\begin{array}{r} 0.4 \\ 5\overline{)2.0} \\ \underline{-20} \\ 0 \end{array}$$

0.4

2. $\frac{8}{9}$

$$\begin{array}{r} 0.\overline{8} \\ 9\overline{)8.0} \\ \underline{-72} \\ 8 \end{array}$$

Because the number 8 repeats during the division process, the answer is a repeating decimal: $0.\overline{8}$.

3. $3\frac{3}{4}$ can also be written as $\frac{15}{4}$, so

$$\begin{array}{r} 3.75 \\ 4\overline{)15.00} \\ \underline{-12} \\ 30 \\ \underline{-28} \\ 20 \\ \underline{-20} \\ 0 \end{array}$$

3.75

4. $\frac{7}{10}$

$$\begin{array}{r} 0.7 \\ 10\overline{)7.0} \\ \underline{-70} \\ 0 \end{array}$$

0.7

5. $2\frac{3}{8}$ can also be written as $\frac{19}{8}$

$$\begin{array}{r} 2.375 \\ 8\overline{)19.000} \\ \underline{-16} \\ 30 \\ \underline{-24} \\ 60 \\ \underline{-56} \\ 40 \\ \underline{-40} \\ 0 \end{array}$$

2.375

6. $\frac{5}{6}$

$$\begin{array}{r} 0.8\overline{3} \\ 6\overline{)5.00} \\ \underline{-48} \\ 20 \\ \underline{-18} \\ 20 \end{array}$$

Because the number 20 repeats during the division process, the answer is a repeating decimal: $0.8\overline{3}$

7. Write the decimal 0.675 as a fraction.

$$0.675 = \frac{675}{1000}$$

Simplify using the same numerator and denominator.

$$\frac{675 \div 25}{1000 \div 25} = \frac{27}{40}$$

8. The decimal 5.6 is the can be written as

$$5 + \frac{6}{10}, \text{ or } 5\frac{3}{5}.$$

9. Write the decimal 0.44 as a fraction.

$$0.44 = \frac{44}{100}$$

Simplify using the same numerator and denominator.

$$\frac{44 \div 4}{100 \div 4} = \frac{11}{25}$$

10. $10x = 4.\overline{4}$
$$\underline{-x \quad -0.\overline{4}}$$
$$9x = 4$$
$$x = \frac{4}{9}$$

11. $100x = 26.\overline{26}$
$$\underline{-x \quad -0.\overline{26}}$$
$$99x = 26$$
$$x = \frac{26}{99}$$

12. $1000x = 325.\overline{325}$
$$\underline{-x \quad -0.\overline{325}}$$
$$999x = 325$$
$$x = \frac{325}{999}$$

13. $x^2 = 144$
$$x = \sqrt{144} = \pm 12$$

14. $x^2 = \frac{25}{289}$
$$x = \sqrt{\frac{25}{289}} = \pm\frac{5}{17}$$

15. $x^3 = 216$
$$x = \sqrt[3]{216} = 6$$

16. $\sqrt{5} \approx 2.25$

17. $\sqrt{3} \approx 1.75$

18. $\sqrt{10} \approx 3.15$

19. Rational numbers can be written in the form $\frac{a}{b}$, where $a$ and $b$ are integers and $b \neq 0$. Irrational numbers cannot be written in this form.

## Independent Practice

20. $\frac{7}{16}$

```
    0.4375
16)7.0000
   -64
    60
   -48
    120
   -112
     80
    -80
      0
```
0.4375 in.

21. $\frac{1}{6}$

```
   0.16
6)1.00
  -6
   40
  -36
   40
```
Because the number 40 repeats during the division process, the answer is a repeating decimal: $0.1\overline{6}$.

22. $2\frac{4}{5}$ can also be written as $\frac{14}{5}$, so

```
   2.8
5)14.0
  -10
   40
  -40
    0
```
The distance is 2.8 km.

23. $98\frac{2}{3}$ can also be written as $\frac{296}{3}$, so

```
   98.6
3)296.00
  -27
   26
  -24
   20
  -18
   20
```
Because the number 20 repeats during the division process, the answer is a repeating decimal: $98.\overline{6}$.

24. Write the decimal 0.8 as a fraction.

$$0.8 = \frac{8}{10}$$

Simplify using the same numerator and denominator.

$$\frac{8 \div 2}{10 \div 2} = \frac{4}{5}$$

A heartbeat takes $\frac{4}{5}$ second.

25. Separate the decimal from 26.2 so that:

$$0.2 = \frac{2}{10}$$

Simplify using the same numerator and denominator.

$$\frac{2 \div 2}{10 \div 2} = \frac{1}{5}$$

Therefore, 26.2 mi = $26\frac{1}{5}$ mi.

26. Separate the repeating digit and let $x = 0.\overline{1}$
$$x = 0.\overline{1}$$
$$(100)x = 100(0.\overline{1})$$
$$100x = 11.\overline{1}$$
$$\underline{-x \quad\quad -0.\overline{1}}$$
$$99x = 11$$
$$x = \frac{11}{99}$$
$$x = \frac{1}{9}$$
Therefore, $72.\overline{1} = 72\frac{1}{9}$.

27. Write the decimal 0.505 as a fraction.

$$0.505 = \frac{505}{1000}$$

Simplify using the same numerator and denominator.

$$\frac{505 \div 5}{1000 \div 5} = \frac{101}{200}$$

A metal penny is worth $\frac{101}{200}$ cent.

28. a. You can set up the equation $x^2 = 400$ to find the length of a side.

   b. $x^2 = 400$
   $\sqrt{x^2} = \sqrt{400}$
   $x = \pm 20$
   The solutions are $x = \pm 20$; the equation has 2 solutions.

   c. The solution $x = 20$ makes sense, but the solution $x = -20$ doesn't make sense, because a painting can't have a side length of $-20$ inches.

   d. The length of the wood trim needed is $4 \times 20 = 80$ inches.

29. His estimate is low because 15 is much closer to 16 than it is to 9. So, a better estimate would be higher, such as 3.8 or 3.9.

30. Sample answer: A good estimate is $x \simeq 4.5$, because $4^3 = 64$ and $5^3 = 125$. Since 95 is about half way between 64 and 125, $\sqrt[3]{95}$ is probably closer to 4.5 than to 4 or 5.

31.
$$V = \frac{4}{3}r^3$$
$$36 = \frac{4}{3}r^3$$
$$36 \div \frac{4}{3} = \frac{4}{3}r^3 \div \frac{4}{3}$$
$$27 = r^3$$
$$\sqrt[3]{27} = \sqrt[3]{r^3}$$
$$3 = r$$
The radius of the sphere is 3 feet.

## Focus on Higher Order Thinking

32. Yes; the cube root of a negative number is always negative, because a negative number cubed is always negative, and a nonnegative number cubed is always nonnegative.

33. $\sqrt{\frac{4}{25}} = \frac{2}{5}$, and $\frac{\sqrt{4}}{\sqrt{25}} = \frac{2}{5}$

   $\sqrt{\frac{16}{81}} = \frac{4}{9}$, and $\frac{\sqrt{16}}{\sqrt{81}} = \frac{4}{9}$

   $\sqrt{\frac{36}{49}} = \frac{6}{7}$, and $\frac{\sqrt{36}}{\sqrt{49}} = \frac{6}{7}$

   Because the expressions yield the same answer, you can see that $\sqrt{\frac{a}{b}} = \frac{\sqrt{a}}{\sqrt{b}}$. Therefore, you can make a conjecture about the multiplication rule for square roots that $\sqrt{a} \cdot \sqrt{b} = \sqrt{a \cdot b}$.

34. The value of a is 225, because the solutions are $x = \pm 15$, and $15 - (-15) = 30$.

## LESSON 1.2

### Your Turn

1. $12\frac{2}{3}$ is a rational number because it can be represented as the ratio $\frac{38}{3}$. It is a real number because all rational numbers are real numbers.

2. The length of the side is $\sqrt{10}$ yd. $\sqrt{10}$ is an irrational number because 10 is a whole number that is not a perfect square. It is a real number because all irrational numbers are real numbers.

3. False. Every integer is a rational number, but not every rational number is an integer. For example, rational numbers such as $\frac{3}{5}$ and $-\frac{5}{2}$ are not integers.

4. False. Real numbers are either rational numbers or irrational numbers. Integers are rational numbers, so no integers are irrational numbers.

5. The set of real numbers best describes the situation. The amount can be any number greater than 0.

6. Possible answer: Real numbers; the number of seconds left can be any number less than 0, depending on the display device.

### Guided Practice

1. $\frac{7}{8}$ is a rational number because it is the ratio of two integers: 7 and 8. It is a real number because all rational numbers are real numbers.

2. $\sqrt{36}$ is a whole number because it is equal to 6, which is a positive number with no fractional or decimal part. Every whole number is also an integer, a rational number, and a real number.

3. $\sqrt{24}$ is an irrational number because 24 is a whole number that is not a perfect square. It is a real number because all irrational numbers are real numbers.

4. 0.75 is a rational number because it is a terminating decimal. It is a real number because all rational numbers are real numbers.

5. 0 is a whole number because it is a number with no fractional or decimal part. Every whole number is also an integer, a rational number, and a real number.

6. $-\sqrt{100}$ is an integer because it is equal to $-10$, which is a number with no fractional or decimal part. Every integer is also a rational number and a real number.

7. $5.\overline{45}$ is a rational number because it is a repeating decimal. It is a real number because all rational numbers are real numbers.

8. $-\frac{18}{6}$ is an integer because it is equal to $-3$, which is a number with no fractional or decimal part. Every integer is also a rational number and a real number.

9. True. Whole numbers are a subset of the set of rational numbers and can be written as a fraction with a denominator of 1.

10. True. Whole numbers are rational numbers.

11. The set of integers best describes the situation. The change can be a whole dollar amount and can be positive, negative, or 0.

12. The set of rational numbers best describes the situation. The ruler is marked every $\frac{1}{16}$ inch.

13. Sample answer: Describe one set as being a subset of another, or show their relationships in a Venn diagram.

## Independent Practice

14. $\sqrt{9}$ is a whole number because it is equal to 3, which is a positive number with no fractional or decimal part. Every whole number is also an integer, a rational number, and a real number.

15. 257 is a whole number because it is a positive number with no fractional or decimal part. Every whole number is also an integer, a rational number, and a real number.

16. $\sqrt{50}$ is an irrational number because 50 is a whole number that is not a perfect square. It is a real number because all irrational numbers are real numbers.

17. $8\frac{1}{2}$ is a rational number because it can be represented as the ratio $\frac{17}{2}$. It is a real number because all rational numbers are real numbers.

18. 16.6 is a rational number because it is a terminating decimal. It is a real number because all rational numbers are real numbers.

19. $\sqrt{16}$ is a whole number because it is equal to 4, which is a positive number with no fractional or decimal part. Every whole number is also an integer, a rational number, and a real number.

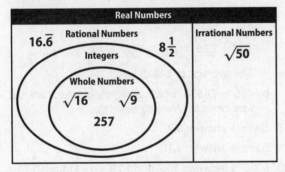

20. The set of real numbers best describes the situation. The height can be any number greater than 0.

21. The set of integers best describes the situation. The scores are counting numbers, their opposites, and 0.

22. Nathaniel is correct. A rational number is a number that can be written as a fraction, and $\frac{1}{11}$ is a fraction.

23. A whole number. The diameter is $\frac{\pi}{\pi}$ mi, or 1 mi.

24. It can be a rational number that is not an integer, or an irrational number.

25. The total number of gallons of milk is either a whole number or a mixed number in which the fractional part is $\frac{1}{2}$. Therefore, the number is a rational number.

## Focus on Higher Order Thinking

26. The set of negative numbers also includes non-integer rational numbers and irrational numbers.

27. Sample answer: If the calculator shows a decimal that terminates in fewer digits than what the calculator screen allows, then you can tell that the number is rational. If not, you cannot tell from the calculator display whether the number terminates because you see a limited number of digits. It may be a repeating decimal (rational) or a non-terminating non-repeating decimal (irrational).

28. It is a whole number. $3 \cdot 0.\overline{3} = 3 \cdot \frac{1}{3} = 1$. Since $3 \cdot 0.\overline{3}$ is equal to $0.\overline{9}$, then $0.\overline{9}$ is equal to 1, which is a whole number.

29. Sample answer: In decimal form, irrational numbers never terminate and never repeat. Therefore, no matter how many decimal places you include, the number will never be precisely represented. There will always be more digits.

## LESSON 1.3

### Your Turn

3. $\sqrt{2}$ is between 1 and 2, so $\sqrt{2} \approx 1.5$.
$\sqrt{2} + 4 \approx 1.5 + 4 = 5.5$
$\sqrt{4} = 2$
$2 + \sqrt{4} = 2 + 2 = 4$
Since $5.5 > 4$, $\sqrt{2} + 4 > 2 + \sqrt{4}$.

4. $\sqrt{12}$ is between 3 and 4, so $\sqrt{12} \approx 3.5$.
$\sqrt{12} + 6 \approx 3.5 + 6 = 9.5$
$\sqrt{6}$ is between 2 and 3, so $\sqrt{6} \approx 2.5$.
$12 + \sqrt{6} \approx 12 + 12.5 = 14.5$
Since $9.5 < 14.5$, $\sqrt{12} + 6 < 12 + \sqrt{6}$.

5. $\sqrt{5}$ is between 2 and 3, but is closer to 2. So $\sqrt{5} < 2.5$.
$\sqrt{3}$ is between 1 and 2, so $\sqrt{3} \approx 1.5$.
$\sqrt{3}, \sqrt{5}, 2.5$

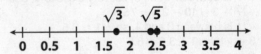

6. An approximate value of $\pi$ is 3.14. So, $\pi^2 \approx 9.8956$.
$\sqrt{75}$ is between 8 and 9, so $\sqrt{75} \approx 8.5$.
$\sqrt{75}, \pi^2, 10$

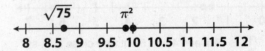

7. $\frac{10}{3} = 3.\overline{3}$; $3\frac{1}{2} = 3.5$
$\sqrt{10}$ is between 3 and 4, but is very close to 3.
So $\sqrt{10} < 3.\overline{3}$.
$3\frac{1}{2}$ mi, $3.\overline{45}$ mi, $\frac{10}{3}$ mi, $\sqrt{10}$ mi

## Guided Practice

1. $\sqrt{3}$ is between 1 and 2, so $\sqrt{3} \approx 1.5$.
   $\sqrt{3} + 2 \approx 1.5 + 2 \approx 3.5$
   $\sqrt{3} + 3 \approx 1.5 + 3 \approx 4.5$
   Since $3.5 < 4.5$, $\sqrt{3} + 2 < \sqrt{3} + 3$.

2. $\sqrt{11}$ is between 3 and 4, so $\sqrt{11} \approx 3.5$.
   $\sqrt{11} + 15 \approx 3.5 + 15 = 18.5$
   $\sqrt{8}$ is between 2 and 3 but very close to 3. Use 2.8.
   $\sqrt{8} + 15 \approx 2.8 + 15 = 17.8$
   Since $18.5 > 17.8$, $\sqrt{11} + 15 > \sqrt{8} + 15$.

3. $\sqrt{6}$ is between 2 and 3, so $\sqrt{6} \approx 2.5$.
   $\sqrt{6} + 5 \approx 2.5 + 5 = 7.5$
   $\sqrt{5}$ is also between 2 and 3, but will be a bit less than 2.5. Use 2.3.
   $6 + \sqrt{5} \approx 6 + 2.3 = 8.3$
   Since $7.5 < 8.3$, $\sqrt{6} + 5 < 6 + \sqrt{5}$.

4. $\sqrt{9} = 3$
   $\sqrt{9} + 3 = 3 + 3 = 6$
   $\sqrt{3}$ is between 1 and 2, so $\sqrt{3} \approx 1.5$.
   $9 + \sqrt{3} \approx 9 + 1.5 = 10.5$
   Since $6 < 10.5$, $\sqrt{9} + 3 < 9 + \sqrt{3}$.

5. $\sqrt{17}$ is between 4 and 5, but very close to 4. Use 4.1.
   $\sqrt{17} - 3 \approx 4.1 - 3 = 1.1$
   $\sqrt{5}$ is between 2 and 3, but very close to 2. Use 2.2.
   $-2 + \sqrt{5} \approx -2 + 2.2 = 0.2$
   Since $1.1 > 0.2$, $\sqrt{17} - 3 > -2 + \sqrt{5}$.

6. $\sqrt{8}$ is between 2 and 3, so $\sqrt{8} \approx 2.5$
   $10 - \sqrt{8} \approx 10 - 2.5 = 7.5$
   $\sqrt{2}$ is between 1 and 2, so $\sqrt{2} \approx 1.5$.
   $12 - \sqrt{2} \approx 12 - 1.5 = 10.5$
   Since $7.5 < 10.5$, $10 - \sqrt{8} < 12 - \sqrt{2}$.

7. $\sqrt{7}$ is between 2 and 3, so $\sqrt{7} \approx 2.5$.
   $\sqrt{7} + 2 \approx 2.5 + 2 = 4.5$
   $\sqrt{10}$ is between 3 and 4, so $\sqrt{10} \approx 3.5$.
   $\sqrt{10} - 1 \approx 3.5 - 1 = 2.5$
   Since $4.5 > 2.5$, $\sqrt{7} + 2 > \sqrt{10} - 1$.

8. $\sqrt{17}$ is between 4 and 5, but very close to 4. Use 4.1.
   $\sqrt{17} + 3 \approx 10 - 2.5 = 7.5$
   $\sqrt{11}$ is between 3 and 4, so $\sqrt{11} \approx 3.5$.
   $3 + \sqrt{11} \approx 3 + 3.5 = 6.5$
   Since $7.5 > 6.5$, $\sqrt{17} + 3 > 3 + \sqrt{11}$.

9. $\sqrt{3}$ is between 1.7 and 1.8, so $\sqrt{3} \approx 1.75$.
   $\pi \approx 3.14$, so $2\pi \approx 6.28$
   $1.5, \sqrt{3}, 2\pi$

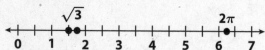

10. $\sqrt{17}$ is between 4 and 5 but very close to 4, so $\sqrt{17} \approx 4.1$, and $\sqrt{17} - 2 \approx 2.1$.

   $\pi \approx 3.14$, so $\frac{\pi}{2} \approx 1.57$, and $1 + \frac{\pi}{2} \approx 2.57$.
   $\frac{12}{5} = 2.4$
   $1 + \frac{\pi}{2}$ km, 2.5 km, $\frac{12}{5}$ km, $\sqrt{17} - 2$ km

11. Sample answer: Convert each number to a decimal equivalent, using estimation to find equivalents for irrational numbers. Graph each number on a number

line. Read the numbers from left to right to order the numbers from least to greatest. Read the numbers from right to left to order the numbers from greatest to least.

## Independent Practice

12. $\sqrt{7}$ is between 2 and 3, so $\sqrt{7} \approx 2.5$.
    $\sqrt{8}$ is between 2 and 3, so $\sqrt{8} \approx 2.5$ and $\frac{\sqrt{8}}{2} \approx 1.75$.
    $\frac{\sqrt{8}}{2}, 2, \sqrt{7}$

13. $\sqrt{10}$ is between 3.1 and 3.2, so $\sqrt{10} \approx 3.15$. $\pi \approx 3.14$.
    $\pi, \sqrt{10}, 3.5$

14. $\sqrt{220}$ is between 14 and 15, so $\sqrt{220} \approx 14.5$.
    $\sqrt{100} = 10$
    $-10, \sqrt{100}, 11.5, \sqrt{220}$

15. $\sqrt{8}$ is between 2 and 3, so $\sqrt{8} \approx 2.5$.
    $\frac{9}{4} = 2.25$
    $-3.75, \frac{9}{4}, \sqrt{8}, 3$

16. a. $A = 3.5^2 = 12.25$ m²
    b. $C = \pi \cdot 4 = 4\pi$ m²
       $4\pi \approx 4 \cdot 3.14 = 12.6$ m²
    c. The circle would give her more space to plant because it has a greater area.

17. a. $\sqrt{60}$ is between 7.7 and 7.8, so $\sqrt{60} \approx 7.75$.
       $\frac{58}{8} = 7.25$
       $7.\overline{3} \approx 7.33$
       $7\frac{3}{5} = 7.60$
       $\frac{7.75 + 7.25 + 7.33 + 7.60}{4} = \frac{29.93}{4} = 7.4825$
       The average is 7.4825 km.
    b. $\sqrt{56} \approx 7.4833$, which is slightly greater than, but very close to, Winnie's estimate.

18. Sample answer: 3.7.

19. Sample answer: $\sqrt{31}$.

20. $\sqrt{115}$ is between 10.7 and 10.8, so $\sqrt{115} \approx 10.75$.
    $\frac{115}{11} = 10.\overline{45}$
    Neither student is correct. The answer should be:
    $\frac{115}{11}, 10.5624, \sqrt{115}$.

21. a. Since $\sqrt{7} \approx 2.65$ and $\sqrt{8} \approx 2.83$, e is between $\sqrt{7}$ and $\sqrt{8}$.
    b. Since $\sqrt{9} = 3$ and $\sqrt{10} \approx 3.16$, $\pi$ is between $\sqrt{9}$ and $\sqrt{10}$.

## Focus on Higher Order Thinking

22. a. $\frac{22}{7} \approx 3.1429$

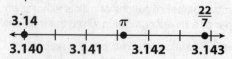

    b. $\frac{22}{7} \approx 3.1429$. It is closer to $\pi$ on the number line.

c. $\frac{x}{113} = 3.1416$

$x = 113 \cdot 3.1416$

$x = 355.0008$

355

23. 2 points; A rational number and an irrational number cannot be represented by the same point on the number line.

24. She did not consider that $12.\overline{6} = 12.66\ldots$ .

## MODULE 1

### Ready to Go On?

1.
$$\begin{array}{r} 0.35 \\ 20\overline{)7.00} \\ \underline{-60} \phantom{0} \\ 100 \\ \underline{-100} \\ 0 \end{array}$$

0.35

2. $x = 1.\overline{27}$

$(100)x = (100)1.\overline{27}$

$100x = 127.\overline{27}$

Because $x = 1.\overline{27}$, subtract $x$ from one side and $1.\overline{27}$ from the other.

$$\begin{array}{r} 100x = 127.\overline{27} \\ \underline{-x \phantom{00} -1.\overline{27}} \\ 99x = 126 \end{array}$$

$\frac{99x}{99} = \frac{126}{99}$

$= \frac{14}{11}$

3. $1\frac{7}{8} = \frac{15}{8}$

$$\begin{array}{r} 1.875 \\ 8\overline{)15.000} \\ \underline{-8} \phantom{.000} \\ 70 \\ \underline{-64} \\ 60 \\ \underline{-56} \\ 40 \\ \underline{-40} \\ 0 \end{array}$$

1.875

4. $\sqrt{81} = 9; -\sqrt{81} = -9$

9 and $-9$

5. $x^3 = 343$

$\sqrt[3]{x^3} = \sqrt[3]{343}$

$x = 7$

6. $\sqrt{\frac{1}{100}} = \frac{1}{10}; -\sqrt{\frac{1}{100}} = -\frac{1}{10}$

$\frac{1}{10}$ and $-\frac{1}{10}$

7. Each side measures $\sqrt{200}$ ft.

$14.1^2 = 198.81; 14.2^2 = 201.64$

so, $\sqrt{200}$ is between 14.1 and 14.2.

$\sqrt{200} \approx 14.15$

Each side is approximately 14.15 feet long.

8. $\frac{121}{\sqrt{121}}$ is a whole number because

$\frac{121}{\sqrt{121}} = \frac{121}{11} = 11$, and 11 is a positive number with no fractional or decimal part. Every whole number is also an integer, a rational number, and a real number.

9. $\frac{\pi}{2}$ is an irrational number because $\pi$ is an irrational number and dividing $\pi$ by 2 gives another irrational number. It is a real number because all irrational numbers are real numbers.

10. True; Integers can be written as the quotient of two integers.

11. $\sqrt{8}$ is between 2 and 3, so $\sqrt{8} \approx 2.5$.

$\sqrt{8} + 3 \approx 2.5 + 3 = 5.5$

$\sqrt{3}$ is between 1 and 2, so $\sqrt{3} \approx 1.5$.

$8 + \sqrt{3} \approx 8 + 1.5 = 9.5$

Since $5.5 < 9.5$, $\sqrt{8} + 3 < 8 + \sqrt{3}$.

12. $\sqrt{5}$ is between 2 and 3, so $\sqrt{5} \approx 2.5$.

$\sqrt{5} + 11 \approx 2.5 + 11 = 13.5$

$\sqrt{11}$ is between 3 and 4, so $\sqrt{11} \approx 3.5$.

$5 + \sqrt{11} \approx 5 + 3.5 = 8.5$

Since $13.5 > 8.5$, $\sqrt{5} + 11 > 5 + \sqrt{11}$.

13. $\pi^2 \approx 9.87$, $9.\overline{8} \approx 9.88$, and $\sqrt{99} \approx 9.95$. Therefore, the order from least to greatest should be $\pi^2$, $9.\overline{8}$, $\sqrt{99}$.

14. $\sqrt{\frac{1}{25}} = \frac{1}{5} = 0.20$

$\frac{1}{4} = 0.25$

$0.\overline{2} = 0.22\ldots$

$\sqrt{\frac{1}{25}}, 0.\overline{2}, \frac{1}{4}$

15. Sample answer: Real numbers, such as the rational number $\frac{1}{4}$, can describe amounts used in cooking.

# MODULE 2 *Exponents and Scientific Notation*

## Are You Ready?

1. $10^2$
   10 × 10
   100

2. $10^3$
   10 × 10 × 10
   1000

3. $10^5$
   10 × 10 × 10 × 10 × 10
   100,000

4. $10^7$
   10 × 10 × 10 × 10 × 10 × 10 × 10
   10,000,000

5. $45.3 \times 10^3$
   45.3 × 1000
   45,300

6. $7.08 \div 10^2$
   7.08 ÷ 100
   0.0708

7. $0.00235 \times 10^6$
   0.00235 × 1,000,000
   2,350

8. $3,600 \div 10^4$
   3,600 ÷ 1,000
   0.36

9. $0.5 \times 10^2$
   0.5 × 100
   50

10. $67.7 \div 10^5$
    67.7 ÷ 100,000
    0.000677

11. $0.0057 \times 10^4$
    0.0057 × 1,000
    57

12. $195 \div 10^6$
    195 ÷ 1,000,000
    0.000195

## LESSON 2.1

### Your Turn

6. $\dfrac{[(6-1)^2]^2}{(3+2)^3}$

   $= \dfrac{[(5)^2]^2}{(5)^3}$

   $= \dfrac{(25)^2}{(5)^3}$

   $= \dfrac{625}{125}$

   $= 5$

7. $(2^2)^3 - (10-6)^3 \cdot 4^{-5}$
   $= (2^2)^3 - 4^3 \cdot 4^{-5}$
   $= 2^6 - 4^3 \cdot 4^{-5}$
   $= 2^6 - 4^{3+(-5)}$
   $= 2^6 - 4^{-2}$
   $= 64 - \dfrac{1}{16}$
   $= 63\dfrac{15}{16}$

## Guided Practice

1. As the exponent decreases by 1, the value of the power is divided by 8.
   $8^0 = 1$
   $8^{-1} = \dfrac{1}{8}$

2. As the exponent decreases by 1, the value of the power is divided by 6.
   $6^0 = 1$
   $6^{-1} = \dfrac{1}{6}$
   $6^{-2} = \dfrac{1}{36}$

3. Any number raised to the power 0 equals 1.
   $256^0 = 1$

4. As the exponent increases by 1, the value of the power is multiplied by 10.
   $10^0 = 1$
   $10^1 = 10$
   $10^2 = 100$

5. As the exponent increases by 1, the value of the power is multiplied by 5.
   $5^0 = 1$
   $5^1 = 5$
   $5^2 = 25$
   $5^3 = 125$
   $5^4 = 625$

6. As the exponent decreases by 1, the value of the power is divided by 2.
   $2^0 = 1$
   $2^{-1} = \dfrac{1}{2}$
   $2^{-2} = \dfrac{1}{4}$
   $2^{-3} = \dfrac{1}{8}$
   $2^{-4} = \dfrac{1}{16}$
   $2^{-5} = \dfrac{1}{32}$

7. As the exponent decreases by 1, the value of the power is divided by 4.
   $4^0 = 1$
   $4^{-1} = \dfrac{1}{4}$
   $4^{-2} = \dfrac{1}{16}$
   $4^{-3} = \dfrac{1}{64}$
   $4^{-4} = \dfrac{1}{256}$
   $4^{-5} = \dfrac{1}{1024}$

8. Any number raised to the power 0 equals 1.

$89^0 = 1$

9. As the exponent decreases by 1, the value of the power is divided by 11.

$$11^0 = 1$$
$$11^{-1} = \frac{1}{11}$$
$$11^{-2} = \frac{1}{121}$$
$$11^{-3} = \frac{1}{1331}$$

10. $4 \cdot 4 \cdot 4$

$$= 4^1 \cdot 4^1 \cdot 4^1$$
$$= 4^{1+1+1}$$
$$= 4^3$$

11. $(2 \cdot 2) \cdot (2 \cdot 2 \cdot 2)$

$$= (2^1 \cdot 2^1) \cdot (2^1 \cdot 2^1 \cdot 2^1)$$
$$= (2^{1+1}) \cdot (2^{1+1+1})$$
$$= 2^2 \cdot 2^3 = 2^5$$

12. $\dfrac{6^7}{6^5}$

$$= \frac{6 \cdot 6 \cdot 6 \cdot 6 \cdot 6 \cdot 6 \cdot 6}{6 \cdot 6 \cdot 6 \cdot 6 \cdot 6}$$
$$= \frac{6^1 \cdot 6^1 \cdot 6^1 \cdot 6^1 \cdot 6^1 \cdot 6^1 \cdot 6^1}{6^1 \cdot 6^1 \cdot 6^1 \cdot 6^1 \cdot 6^1}$$
$$= \frac{6^{1+1+1+1+1+1+1}}{6^{1+1+1+1+1}}$$
$$= \frac{6^7}{6^5}$$
$$= 6^{7-5}$$
$$= 6^2$$

13. $\dfrac{8^{12}}{8^9}$

$$= 8^{12-9}$$
$$= 8^3$$

14. $5^{10} \cdot 5 \cdot 5$

$$= 5^{10} \cdot 5^1 \cdot 5^1$$
$$= 5^{10+1+1}$$
$$= 5^{12}$$

15. $7^8 \cdot 7^5$

$$= 7^{8+5}$$
$$= 7^{13}$$

16. $(6^2)^4$

$$= (6^{1+1})^4$$
$$= (6^1 \cdot 6^1)^4$$
$$= (6 \cdot 6)^4$$
$$= (6 \cdot 6) \cdot (6 \cdot 6) \cdot (6 \cdot 6) \cdot (6 \cdot 6)$$
$$= 6^8$$

17. $(3^3)^3$

$$= (3^{1+1+1})^3$$
$$= (3^1 \cdot 3^1 \cdot 3^1)^3$$
$$= (3 \cdot 3 \cdot 3)^3$$
$$= (3 \cdot 3 \cdot 3) \cdot (3 \cdot 3 \cdot 3) \cdot (3 \cdot 3 \cdot 3)$$
$$= 3^9$$

18. $(10 - 6)^3 \cdot 4^2 + (10 + 2)^2$

$$= 4^3 \cdot 4^2 + 12^2$$
$$= 4^{3+2} + 12^2$$
$$= 4^5 + 12^2$$
$$= 1{,}024 + 144$$
$$= 1{,}168$$

19. $\dfrac{(12 - 5)^7}{[(3 + 4)^2]^2}$

$$= \frac{7^7}{(7^2)^2}$$
$$= \frac{7^7}{7^{2 \cdot 2}}$$
$$= \frac{7^7}{7^4}$$
$$= 7^{7-4}$$
$$= 7^3$$
$$= 343$$

20. Sample answer: When multiplying powers with the same base, you add the exponents. When dividing powers with the same base, you subtract the exponents. When raising a power to a power, you multiply the exponents.

**Independent Practice**

21. The exponents cannot be added because the bases are not the same.

22. To express $3^5$ as a product of powers, the bases should be 3 and the powers should add up to 5; Sample answer: $3^5 \cdot 3^0$; $3^4 \cdot 3^1$; $3^3 \cdot 3^2$

23. $22^7 > 22^4$;

$$\frac{22^7}{22^4}$$
$$= 22^{7-4}$$
$$= 22^3$$
$$= 10{,}648$$

The distance from Earth to Neptune is the greater distance. It is about 10,648 times greater than the distance from Earth to the moon.

24. The student is not correct because

$8^3 \cdot 8^{-5} = 8^{3+(-5)} = 8^{-2} = \dfrac{1}{8^2} = \dfrac{1}{64}$, which is less than 1.

25. $(b^2)^n = b^{-6}$

$$2n = -6$$
$$\frac{2n}{2} = \frac{-6}{2}$$
$$n = -3$$
$$(b^2)^{-3} = b^{-6}$$

26. $x^m \cdot x^6 = x^9$

$$m + 6 = 9$$
$$m + 6 - 6 = 9 - 6$$
$$m = 3$$
$$x^3 \cdot x^6 = x^9$$

27. $\dfrac{y^{25}}{y^n} = y^6$

$$25 - n = 6$$
$$25 - n - 25 = 6 - 25$$
$$-n = -19$$
$$-n \cdot (-1) = -19 \cdot (-1)$$
$$n = 19$$
$$\dfrac{y^{25}}{y^{19}} = y^6$$

28. Sample answer: Dividing is the same as multiplying by the reciprocal. So when dividing powers with the same base, you add the opposite of the exponent in the denominator. This is the same as subtracting the exponents.

29. $\dfrac{2 \times 10^{30}}{2 \times 10^{27}}$

$= \dfrac{10^{30}}{10^{27}}$

$= 10^{30-27}$

$= 10^3$

$= 1{,}000$

$10^3$ kg, or 1,000 kg

30. $2^{10} \cdot 2^{30}$
$= 2^{10+30}$
$= 2^{40}$
$2^{40}$ bytes

31. $x^7 \cdot x^{-2}$
$= x^{7+(-2)}$
$= x^5;$
$= \dfrac{x^7}{x^2}$
$= x^{7-2}$
$= x^5$

Both expressions equal $x^5$, so $x^7 \cdot x^{-2} = \dfrac{x^7}{x^2}$; Sample answer: When multiplying powers with the same base, you add exponents: $7 + (-2) = 5$. When dividing powers with the same base, you subtract exponents: $7 - 2 = 5$. In cases like this, $x^n \cdot x^{-m} = \dfrac{x^n}{x^m}$.

32. The number of cubes in each row is 3 raised to the row number.

33. Since the number of cubes in each row is 3 raised to the row number, the number of cubes in Row 6 will be 3 raised to the power 6, and the number of cubes in Row 3 will be 3 raised to the power 3.
$3^6 = 729;$
$\dfrac{3^6}{3^3}$
$= 3^{6-3}$
$= 3^3$
$= 27$
The number of cubes in Row 6 will be $3^6$, or 729. There will be $3^3$, or 27, times the number of cubes in Row 6 as there are in Row 3.

34. $3^1 + 3^2 + 3^3 + 3^4 + 3^5 + 3^6$
$= 3 + 9 + 27 + 81 + 243 + 729$
$= 1{,}092$
The total number of cubes in the triangle is 1,092; Sample answer: I evaluated $3^1$, $3^2$, $3^3$, $3^4$, $3^5$, and $3^6$ and added these numbers together.

## Focus on Higher Order Thinking

35. Sample answer: No, I do not agree, because
$$\dfrac{6^2}{36^2} = \dfrac{6 \cdot 6}{36 \cdot 36} = \dfrac{6 \cdot 6}{6 \cdot 6 \cdot 6 \cdot 6} = \dfrac{1}{6 \cdot 6} = \dfrac{1}{36}.$$

36. $-3^2 = -9$
$-3^3 = -27$
$-3^4 = -81$
$-3^5 = -243;$
$(-3)^2 = 9$
$(-3)^3 = -27$
$(-3)^4 = 81$
$(-3)^5 = -243$
For $-a^n$, you get $-9$, $-27$, $-81$, and $-243$.
For $(-a)^n$, you get $9$, $-27$, $81$, and $-243$. No, it does not appear that $-a^n = (-a)^n$. When $n$ is even, the two expressions are opposites. When $n$ is odd, the two expressions are equal.

37. Let the number equal $x$.
$$\dfrac{x^{12}}{x^9} = 125$$
$$x^{12-9} = 125$$
$$x^3 = 125$$
The cube root of 125 is the number 5.

## LESSON 2.2

### Your Turn

3. Move the decimal in 6,400 to the left to get 6.4.
$6{,}400 \div 6.4 = 1{,}000 = 10^3$
$6{,}400 = 6.4 \times 10^3$

4. Move the decimal in 570,000,000,000 to the left to get 5.7.
$570{,}000{,}000{,}000 \div 5.7 = 100{,}000{,}000{,}000 = 10^{11}$
$570{,}000{,}000{,}000 = 5.7 \times 10^{11}$

5. Move the decimal in 9,461,000,000,000 to the left to get 9.461.
$9{,}461{,}000{,}000{,}000 \div 9.461 = 1{,}000{,}000{,}000{,}000 = 10^{12}$
$9{,}461{,}000{,}000{,}000 = 9.461 \times 10^{12}$ km

8. To write $7.034 \times 10^9$ in standard notation, move the decimal 9 places to the right.
$7.034 \times 10^9 = 7{,}034{,}000{,}000$

9. To write $2.36 \times 10^5$ in standard notation, move the decimal 5 places to the right.
$2.36 \times 10^5 = 236{,}000$

10. To write $5 \times 10^6$ in standard notation, move the decimal 6 places to the right.
$5 \times 10^6 = 5{,}000{,}000$ g

## Guided Practice

1. Move the decimal in 58,927 to the left to get 5.8927.
$$58,927 \div 5.8927 = 10,000 = 10^4$$
$$58,927 = 5.8927 \times 10^4$$

2. Move the decimal in 1,304,000,000 to the left to get 1.304.
$$1,304,000,000 \div 1.304 = 1,000,000,000 = 10^9$$
$$1,304,000,000 = 1.304 \times 10^9$$

3. Move the decimal in 6,730,000 to the left to get 6.73.
$$6,730,000 \div 6.73 = 1,000,000 = 10^6$$
$$6,730,000 = 6.73 \times 10^6$$

4. Move the decimal in 13,300 to the left to get 1.33.
$$13,300 \div 1.33 = 10,000 = 10^4$$
$$13,300 = 1.33 \times 10^4$$

5. Move the decimal in 97,700,000,000,000,000,000,000 to the left to get 9.77.
$$97,700,000,000,000,000,000,000 \div 9.77 = 10^{22}$$
$$97,700,000,000,000,000,000,000 = 9.77 \times 10^{22}$$

6. Move the decimal in 384,000 to the left to get 3.84.
$$384,000 \div 3.84 = 100,000 = 10^5$$
$$384,000 = 3.84 \times 10^5$$

7. To write $4 \times 10^5$ in standard notation, move the decimal 5 places to the right.
$$4 \times 10^5 = 400,000$$

8. To write $1.8499 \times 10^9$ in standard notation, move the decimal 9 places to the right.
$$1.8499 \times 10^9 = 1,849,900,000$$

9. To write $6.41 \times 10^3$ in standard notation, move the decimal 3 places to the right.
$$6.41 \times 10^3 = 6,410$$

10. To write $8.456 \times 10^7$ in standard notation, move the decimal 7 places to the right.
$$8.456 \times 10^7 = 84,560,000$$

11. To write $8 \times 10^5$ in standard notation, move the decimal 5 places to the right.
$$8 \times 10^5 = 800,000$$

12. To write $9 \times 10^{10}$ in standard notation, move the decimal 10 places to the right.
$$9 \times 10^{10} = 90,000,000,000$$

13. To write $5.4 \times 10^4$ in standard notation, move the decimal 4 places to the right.
$$5.4 \times 10^4 = 54,000 \text{ s}$$

14. To write $7.6 \times 10^6$ in standard notation, move the decimal 6 places to the right.
$$7.6 \times 10^6 = 7,600,000 \text{ cans}$$

15. First move the decimal 9 places to the left to find 3.482, a number that is greater than or equal to 1 and less than 10. Then multiply 3.482 by $10^9$, using an exponent on 10 that equals the number of places you moved the decimal.

## Independent Practice

16. Move the decimal in 66,000 to the left to get 6.6.
$$66,000 \div 6.6 = 10,000 = 10^4$$
$$66,000 = 6.6 \times 10^4 \text{ lb}$$

17. Move the decimal in 220,000 to the left to get 2.2.
$$220,000 \div 2.2 = 100,000 = 10^5$$
$$220,000 = 2.2 \times 10^5 \text{ lb}$$

18. Move the decimal in 100,000 to the left to get 1.
$$100,000 \div 1 = 100,000 = 10^5$$
$$100,000 = 1 \times 10^5 \text{ lb}$$

19. Move the decimal in 40,000 to the left to get 4.
$$40,000 \div 4 = 10,000 = 10^4$$
$$40,000 = 4 \times 10^4 \text{ lb}$$

20. Move the decimal in 19,850 to the left to get 1.985.
$$19,850 \div 1.985 = 10,000 = 10^4$$
$$19,850 = 1.985 \times 10^4 \text{ lb}$$

21. Move the decimal in 50,000 to the left to get 5.
$$50,000 \div 5 = 10,000 = 10^4$$
$$50,000 = 5 \times 10^4 \text{ lb}$$

22. $$1,000 \times 10.5 = 10,500$$
$$10,500 \div 1.05 = 10,000 = 10^4$$
$$10,500 = 1.05 \times 10^4 \text{ mosquitoes}$$

23. $$\frac{40 \text{ words} \times 60}{1 \text{ minute} \times 60} = \frac{2,400 \text{ words}}{1 \text{ hour}}$$
$$2.6 \times 10^5 = 260,000$$
$$260,000 \div 2,400 = 108.\overline{3}$$
$108\frac{1}{3}$ hours, or 108 hours and 20 minutes

24. a. Write 1.182 in standard notation, 1,182, and then multiply by your weight.

    b. Sample answer: 94,560 lb; $9.456 \times 10^4$

25. $$230 \times 20 = 4,600$$
$$4,600 \div 4.6 = 1,000 = 10^3$$
$$4,600 = 4.6 \times 10^3 \text{ lb}$$

26. $9.999 \times 10^4$ and $2 \times 10^1$; numbers in scientific notation are written as the product of a number greater than or equal to 1 and less than 10, and a power of 10, so $0.641 \times 10^3$ and $4.38 \times 5^{10}$ are not written in scientific notation.

27. a. None of the girls have the correct answer.

    b. Polly and Samantha have the decimal in the wrong places, causing their exponents to be incorrect. Esther has the decimal in the correct place but miscounted the number of places the decimal moved.

28. Sample answer: Scientific notation is a quicker way to write large numbers. Also, it's easier to read, it's used by scientists everywhere, and it's easy to compare sizes of large numbers written in scientific notation.

## Focus on Higher Order Thinking

29. The speed of a car because it is likely to be less than 100.

30. $2.1 \times 10^8$ is greater because the exponent 8 is greater than the exponent 6.

31. Is the first factor greater than or equal to 1 and less than 10? Is the second factor a power of 10?

# LESSON 2.3

## Your Turn

4. Move the decimal in 0.0000829 to the right 5 places to get 8.29.
   $0.0000829 = 8.29 \times 10^{-5}$

5. Move the decimal in 0.000000302 to the right 7 places to get 3.02.
   $0.000000302 = 3.02 \times 10^{-7}$

6. Move the decimal in 0.000007 to the right 6 places to get 7.
   $0.000007 = 7 \times 10^{-6}$ m

9. Move the decimal in 1.045 to the left 6 places.
   $1.045 \times 10^{-6} = 0.000001045$

10. Move the decimal in 9.9 to the left 5 places.
    $9.9 \times 10^{-5} = 0.000099$

11. Move the decimal to the left 2 places.
    $1 \times 10^{-2} = 0.01$ m

## Guided Practice

1. Move the decimal in 0.000487 to the right 4 places to get 4.87.
   $0.000487 = 4.87 \times 10^{-4}$

2. Move the decimal in 0.000028 to the right 5 places to get 2.8.
   $0.000028 = 2.8 \times 10^{-5}$

3. Move the decimal in 0.000059 to the right 5 places to get 5.9.
   $0.000059 = 5.9 \times 10^{-5}$

4. Move the decimal in 0.0417 to the right 2 places to get 4.17.
   $0.0417 = 4.17 \times 10^{-2}$

5. Move the decimal in 0.00002 to the right 5 places to get 2.
   $0.00002 = 2 \times 10^{-5}$

6. Move the decimal in 0.000015 to the right 5 places to get 1.5.
   $0.000015 = 1.5 \times 10^{-5}$

7. Move the decimal to the left 5 places.
   $2 \times 10^{-5} = 0.00002$

8. Move the decimal in 3.582 to the left 6 places.
   $3.582 \times 10^{-6} = 0.000003582$

9. Move the decimal in 8.3 to the left 4 places.
   $8.3 \times 10^{-4} = 0.00083$

10. Move the decimal in 2.97 to the left 2 places.
    $2.97 \times 10^{-2} = 0.0297$

11. Move the decimal in 9.06 to the left 5 places.
    $9.06 \times 10^{-5} = 0.0000906$

12. Move the decimal to the left 5 places.
    $4 \times 10^{-5} = 0.00004$

13. Move the decimal in 0.0001 to the right 4 places to get 1.
    $0.0001 = 1 \times 10^{-4}$

14. Move the decimal to the left 24 places.
    $1.7 \times 10^{-24} = 0.0000000000000000000000017$

15. Move the decimal point 5 places right to find 6.72, a number greater than or equal to 1 and less than 10. Then multiply 6.72 by $10^{-5}$, using a negative exponent on 10 that equals the number of places you moved the decimal.

## Independent Practice

16. Move the decimal in 0.00277 to the right 3 places to get 2.77.
    $0.00277 = 2.77 \times 10^{-3}$ cm

17. Move the decimal in 0.0013 to the right 3 places to get 1.3.
    $0.0013 = 1.3 \times 10^{-3}$ cm

18. Move the decimal in 0.0035 to the right 3 places to get 3.5.
    $0.0035 = 3.5 \times 10^{-3}$ cm

19. Move the decimal in 0.0045 to the right 3 places to get 4.5.
    $0.0045 = 4.5 \times 10^{-3}$ cm

20. Move the decimal in 0.015 to the right 2 places to get 1.5.
    $0.015 = 1.5 \times 10^{-2}$ cm

21. Move the decimal in 0.0008 to the right 4 places to get 8.
    $0.0008 = 8 \times 10^{-4}$ cm

22. The ounces in a cup of milk; it is more than 1 but less than 10.

23. 7 cm = 0.07 m, 7 cm = $7 \times 10^0$ cm; 0.07 m $= 7 \times 10^{-2}$ m. The first factors are the same; the exponents differ by 2.

24. 1.89E−12; the exponent on 10

25. If the exponent on 10 is nonnegative, the number is greater than or equal to 1.

26. Move the decimal in 0.000047 to the right 5 places to get 4.7.
    $0.000047 = 4.7 \times 10^{-5}$ L

27. Negative, because a ladybug would weigh less than 1 ounce.

28. Move the decimal in 1,740,000 to the left to get 1.74.
    $1,740,000 \div 1.74 = 1,000,000 = 10^6$
    $1,740,000 = 1.74 \times 10^6$

29. Move the decimal in 1.25 to the left 10 places.
    $1.25 \times 10^{-10} = 0.000000000125$

30. Move the decimal in 0.0028 to the right 3 places to get 2.8.
    $0.0028 = 2.8 \times 10^{-3}$

31. To write $7.149 \times 10^7$ in standard notation, move the decimal 7 places to the right.
    $7.149 \times 10^7 = 71,490,000$

32. Move the decimal in 0.000000000182 to the right 10 places to get 1.82.
    $0.000000000182 = 1.82 \times 10^{-10}$

33. To write $3.397 \times 10^6$ in standard notation, move the decimal 5 places to the right.
$3.397 \times 10^6 = 3,397,000$

34. Atom of silver, atom of aluminum, Atlantic wolfish egg, the Moon, Mars, Jupiter

### Focus on Higher Order Thinking

35. $1.5 \times 10^{-2} = 0.015$
$1.2 \times 10^2 = 120$
$5.85 \times 10^{-3} = 0.00585$
$2.3 \times 10^{-2} = 0.023$
$9.6 \times 10^{-1} = 0.96$
$5.85 \times 10^{-3}$ m, $1.5 \times 10^{-2}$ m, $2.3 \times 10^{-2}$ m, $9.6 \times 10^{-1}$ m, $1.2 \times 10^2$ m

36. Al treated the exponent as if it were positive instead of negative and moved the decimal in the wrong direction. The answer should be 0.00000056.

37. The number will be greater than 1 because you are dividing a number that is greater than or equal to 1 by a decimal value less than 1.

## LESSON 2.4

### Your Turn

1. $(1.1 \times 10^8) - (3.38 \times 10^7)$
$= (1.1 \times 10^8) - (0.338 \times 10^8)$
$= (1.1 - 0.388) \times 10^8$
$= 0.762 \times 10^8$
$= 7.62 \times 10^7$
$7.62 \times 10^7$ more people live in Mexico than in Canada.

2. $(1.86 \times 10^5) \times (4.8 \times 10^3)$
$= (1.86 \times 4.8) \times (10^5 \times 10^3)$
$= (1.86 \times 4.8) \times 10^{5+3}$
$= 8.928 \times 10^8$
The approximate distance from the Sun to Saturn is $8.928 \times 10^8$ miles.

3. $\dfrac{3,670,000,000}{1.17 \times 10^7}$
$= \dfrac{3.67 \times 10^9}{1.17 \times 10^7}$
$= \dfrac{3.67}{1.17} \times \dfrac{10^9}{10^7}$
$= \dfrac{3.67}{1.17} \times 10^{9-7}$
$= 3.14 \times 10^2$
On average, it takes sunlight $3.14 \times 10^2$ minutes to reach Pluto.

4. The letter "E" takes the place of "× 10".
$7.5 \times 10^5 = 7.5E5$

5. The letter "E" takes the place of "× 10".
$3 \times 10^{-7} = 3E-7$

6. The letter "E" takes the place of "× 10".
$2.7 \times 10^{13} = 2.7E13$

7. "× 10" takes the place of the letter "E".
$4.5E-1 = 4.5 \times 10^{-1}$

8. "× 10" takes the place of the letter "E".
$5.6E12 = 5.6 \times 10^{12}$

9. "× 10" takes the place of the letter "E".
$6.98E-8 = 6.98 \times 10^{-8}$

### Guided Practice

1. $4.2 \times 10^6 + 2.25 \times 10^5 + 2.8 \times 10^6$
$= 4.2 \times 10^6 + 0.225 \times 10^6 + 2.8 \times 10^6$
$= (4.2 + 0.225 + 2.8) \times 10^6$
$= 7.225 \times 10^6$

2. $8.5 \times 10^3 - 5.3 \times 10^3 - 1.0 \times 10^2$
$= 8.5 \times 10^3 - 5.3 \times 10^3 - 0.10 \times 10^3$
$= (8.5 - 5.3 - 0.10) \times 10^3$
$= 3.1 \times 10^3$

3. $1.25 \times 10^2 + 0.50 \times 10^2 + 3.25 \times 10^2$
$= (1.25 + 0.50 + 3.25) \times 10^2$
$= 5 \times 10^2$

4. $6.2 \times 10^5 - 2.6 \times 10^4 - 1.9 \times 10^2$
$= 6.2 \times 10^5 - 0.26 \times 10^5 - 0.0019 \times 10^5$
$= (6.2 - 0.26 - 0.0019) \times 10^5$
$= 5.9381 \times 10^5$

5. $(1.8 \times 10^9)(6.7 \times 10^{12})$
$= (1.8 \times 6.7) \times (10^9 \times 10^{12})$
$= (1.8 \times 6.7) \times 10^{9+12}$
$= 12.06 \times 10^{21}$
$= 1.206 \times 10^{22}$

6. $\dfrac{3.46 \times 10^{17}}{2 \times 10^9}$
$= \dfrac{3.46}{2} \times \dfrac{10^{17}}{10^9}$
$= \dfrac{3.46}{2} \times 10^{17-9}$
$= 1.73 \times 10^8$

7. $(5 \times 10^{12})(3.38 \times 10^6)$
$= (5 \times 3.38) \times (10^{12} \times 10^6)$
$= (5 \times 3.38) \times 10^{12+6}$
$= 16.9 \times 10^{18}$
$= 1.69 \times 10^{19}$

8. $\dfrac{8.4 \times 10^{21}}{4.2 \times 10^{14}}$
$= \dfrac{8.4}{4.2} \times \dfrac{10^{21}}{10^{14}}$
$= \dfrac{8.4}{4.2} \times 10^{21-14}$
$= 2 \times 10^7$

9. The letter "E" takes the place of "× 10".
$3.6 \times 10^{11} = 3.6E11$

10. The letter "E" takes the place of "× 10".
$7.25 \times 10^{-5} = 7.25E-5$

11. The letter "E" takes the place of "× 10".
$8 \times 10^{-1} = 8E-1$

12. "× 10" takes the place of the letter "E".
$7.6E-4 = 7.6 \times 10^{-4}$

13. "× 10" takes the place of the letter "E".
$1.2E16 = 1.2 \times 10^{16}$

14. "× 10" takes the place of the letter "E".
$9E1 = 9 \times 10^1$

15. Sample answer: To add or subtract, rewrite the numbers to the same power of 10, add or subtract the multipliers, and rewrite the answer is scientific notation. To multiply or divide, multiply or divide the multipliers, use the rules of exponents to multiply or divide the powers of 10, and rewrite the answer in scientific notation.

## Independent Practice

16. $(4.0 \times 10^7) \times (3.65 \times 10^2)$
$= (4.0 \times 3.65) \times (10^7 \times 10^2)$
$= (4.0 \times 3.65) \times 10^{7+2}$
$= 14.6 \times 10^9$
$= 1.46 \times 10^{10}$
An adult blue whale can eat $1.46 \times 10^{10}$ krill in $3.65 \times 10^2$ days.

17. $\dfrac{4.94 \times 10^{13}}{26,000,000,000}$
$= \dfrac{4.94 \times 10^{13}}{2.6 \times 10^{10}}$
$= \dfrac{4.94}{2.6} \times \dfrac{10^{13}}{10^{10}}$
$= \dfrac{4.94}{2.6} \times 10^{13-10}$
$= 1.9 \times 10^3$
An adult has about $1.9 \times 10^3$ as many cells as a newborn.

18. $(7.131 \times 10^7) + (1.153 \times 10^7) + (3.104 \times 10^7)$
$= (7.131 + 1.153 + 3.104) \times 10^7$
$= 11.388 \times 10^7$
$= 1.1388 \times 10^8$
The total amount of paper, glass, and plastic waste generated is $1.1388 \times 10^8$ tons.

19. $(4.457 \times 10^7) + (0.313 \times 10^7) + (0.255 \times 10^7)$
$= (4.457 + 0.313 + 0.255) \times 10^7$
$= 5.025 \times 10^7$
The total amount of paper, glass, and plastic waste recovered is $5.025 \times 10^7$ tons.

20. $(1.1388 \times 10^8) - (5.025 \times 10^7)$
$= (1.1388 \times 10^8) - (0.5025 \times 10^8)$
$= (1.1388 - 0.5025) \times 10^8$
$= 0.6363 \times 10^8$
$= 6.363 \times 10^7$
The total amount of paper, glass, and plastic waste not recovered is $6.363 \times 10^7$ tons.

21. Paper:
$\dfrac{4.457 \times 10^7}{7.137 \times 10^7}$
$= \dfrac{4.457}{7.131} \times 10^{7-7}$
$= 0.625 \times 10^0$
$= 0.625 \times 1$
$= 0.625$
Glass:
$\dfrac{0.313 \times 10^7}{1.153 \times 10^7}$
$= \dfrac{0.313}{1.153} \times 10^{7-7}$
$= 0.271 \times 10^0$
$= 0.271 \times 1$
$= 0.271$

Plastics:
$\dfrac{0.255 \times 10^7}{3.104 \times 10^7}$
$= \dfrac{0.255}{3.104} \times 10^{7-7}$
$= 0.082 \times 10^0$
$= 0.082 \times 1$
$= 0.082$
Plastics have the lowest recovery ratio.

22. $(6.48 \times 10^7) - (2.15 \times 10^7)$
$= (6.48 - 2.15) \times 10^7$
$= 4.33 \times 10^7$
$4.33 \times 10^7$ more people live in France than Australia.

23. $\dfrac{2.15 \times 10^7}{2.95 \times 10^6}$
$= \dfrac{2.15}{2.95} \times \dfrac{10^7}{10^6}$
$= \dfrac{2.15}{2.95} \times 10^{7-6}$
$= 0.7 \times 10^1$
$= 0.7 \times 10$
$= 7$
The approximate average number of people per square mile in Australia is 7.

24. $\dfrac{1.3 \times 10^9}{6.48 \times 10^7}$
$= \dfrac{1.3}{6.48} \times \dfrac{10^9}{10^7}$
$= \dfrac{1.3}{6.48} \times 10^{9-7}$
$= 0.201 \times 10^2$
$= 2.01 \times 10^1$
$= 20.1$
The population of China is about 20.1 times as great as the population of France.

25. First convert Mia's age to hours.
$\dfrac{7.01568 \times 10^6}{60}$
$= \dfrac{7.01568 \times 10^6}{6 \times 10^1}$
$= \dfrac{7.01568}{6} \times \dfrac{10^6}{10^1}$
$= \dfrac{7.01568}{6} \times 10^{6-1}$
$= 1.16928 \times 10^5$

Next, convert Mia's age to days.
$\dfrac{1.16928 \times 10^5}{24}$
$= \dfrac{1.16928 \times 10^5}{2.4 \times 10^1}$
$= \dfrac{1.16928}{2.4} \times \dfrac{10^5}{10^1}$
$= \dfrac{1.16928}{2.4} \times 10^{5-1}$
$= 0.4872 \times 10^4$
$= 4.872 \times 10^3$
$= 4,872$

If each year has six 30-day months and six 31-day months, the average number of days in a month is 30.5. Convert 4872 days to years.

$$4872 \text{ days} \cdot \frac{1 \text{ month}}{30.5 \text{ days}} \cdot \frac{1 \text{ year}}{12 \text{ months}}$$
$$= 13.311475 \text{ years}$$

Convert the fraction of years into months:

$$0.311475 \text{ years} \cdot \frac{12 \text{ months}}{1 \text{ year}} = 3.7377049 \text{ months}$$

Convert the fraction of months into days:

$$0.7377049 \text{ months} \cdot \frac{30.5 \text{ days}}{1 \text{ month}} = 22.4\overline{9} \text{ days}$$

Mia is 13 years, 3 months, and 22.5 days old.

26. $(2.4 \times 10^4) \times 810$
$= (2.4 \times 10^4) \times (8.1 \times 10^2)$
$= (2.4 \times 8.1) \times (10^4 \times 10^2)$
$= (2.4 \times 8.1) \times 10^{4+2}$
$= 19.44 \times 10^6$
$= 1.944 \times 10^7$

There are 1,000,000 millimeters in a kilometer, so to convert millimeters to kilometers, divide the number of millimeters by 1,000,000.

$$\frac{1.944 \times 10^7}{1,000,000}$$

$$= \frac{1.944 \times 10^7}{1 \times 10^6}$$

$$= \frac{1.944}{1} \times \frac{10^7}{10^6}$$

$= 1.944 \times 10^1$
$= 1.944 \times 10$
$= 19.44$

Courtney covered $1.944 \times 10^7$ mm or 19.44 km during her run.

27. $\dfrac{9.06 \times 10^{12}}{3.08 \times 10^8}$

$= \dfrac{9.06}{3.08} \times \dfrac{10^{12}}{10^8}$

$= \dfrac{9.06}{3.08} \times 10^{12-8}$

$= 2.94 \times 10^4$

$= 29,400$

The average US public debt per American was $2.94 \times 10^4$ or \$29,400 per person in October 2010.

**Focus on Higher Order Thinking**

28. Sample answer: You can add or subtract numbers written in scientific notation only if their powers of 10 are the same. You can multiply and divide numbers written in scientific notation that have different powers. The laws of exponents are used to combine the powers.

29. $(8 \times 10^6) \times (5 \times 10^9)$
$= (8 \times 5) \times (10^6 \times 10^9)$
$= (8 \times 5) \times 10^{6+9}$
$= 40 \times 10^{15}$
$= 4 \times 10^{16}$

The student was off by a power of 10. The correct product is $4 \times 10^{16}$.

30. $\dfrac{(4.87 \times 10^{12}) - (7 \times 10^{10})}{(3 \times 10^7) + (6.1 \times 10^8)}$

$= \dfrac{(487 \times 10^{10}) - (7 \times 10^{10})}{(3 \times 10^7) + (6.1 \times 10^8)}$

$= \dfrac{(487 - 7) \times 10^{10}}{(3 \times 10^7) + (6.1 \times 10^8)}$

$= \dfrac{480 \times 10^{10}}{(3 \times 10^7) + (6.1 \times 10^8)}$

$= \dfrac{4.8 \times 10^{12}}{(3 \times 10^7) + (6.1 \times 10^8)}$

$= \dfrac{4.8 \times 10^{12}}{(3 \times 10^7) + (61 \times 10^7)}$

$= \dfrac{4.8 \times 10^{12}}{(3 + 61) \times 10^7}$

$= \dfrac{4.8 \times 10^{12}}{64 \times 10^7}$

$= \dfrac{4.8}{6.4} \times \dfrac{10^{12}}{10^8}$

$= \dfrac{4.8}{6.4} \times 10^{12-8}$

$= 0.75 \times 10^4$

$= 7.5 \times 10^3$

Sample answer: First, simplify the numerator by rewriting both numbers to the same power of 10 $(10^{10})$ and subtracting to get $480 \times 10^{10}$ or $4.8 \times 10^{12}$. Then simplify the denominator by rewriting both numbers to the same power of $10 (10^7)$ and adding to get $64 \times 10^7$ or $6.4 \times 10^8$. Finally, divide the multipliers $(4.8 \div 6.4)$ to get 0.75, use the division rule for exponents $\left(\dfrac{10^{12}}{10^8}\right)$ to get $10^4$, and rewrite $0.75 \times 10^4$ in scientific notation as $7.5 \times 10^3$.

## MODULE 2

### Ready to Go On?

1. As the exponent decreases by 1, the value of the power is divided by 3.
$3^0 = 1$
$3^{-1} = \dfrac{1}{3}$
$3^{-2} = \dfrac{1}{9}$
$3^{-3} = \dfrac{1}{27}$
$3^{-4} = \dfrac{1}{81}$

2. Any number raised to the power 0 equals 1.
$35^0 = 1$

3. As the exponent increases by 1, the value of the power is multiplied by 4.
$4^0 = 1$
$4^1 = 4$
$4^2 = 16$
$4^3 = 64$
$4^4 = 256$

4. $8^3 \cdot 8^7$
$= 8^{3+7}$
$= 8^{10}$

5. $\dfrac{12^6}{12^2}$
$= 12^{6-2}$
$= 12^4$

6. $\left(10^3\right)^5$
$= 10^{3 \times 5}$
$= 10^{15}$

7. 2,000
Move the decimal point in 2,000 to the left 3 places to get 2.
$2{,}000 = 2 \times 10^3$

8. 91,007,500
Move the decimal point in 91,007,500 to the left 7 places to get 9.10075.
$91{,}007{,}500 = 9.10075 \times 10^7$

9. To write $1.0395 \times 10^9$ in standard notation, move the decimal point 9 places to the right.
$1.0395 \times 10^9 = 1{,}039{,}500{,}000$

10. To write $4 \times 10^2$ in standard notation, move the decimal point 2 places to the right.
$4 \times 10^2 = 400$

11. Move the decimal point in 0.02 to the right 2 places to get 2.
$0.02 = 2 \times 10^{-2}$

12. Move the decimal point in 0.000701 to the right 4 places to get 7.01.
$0.000701 = 7.01 \times 10^{-4}$

13. To write $8.9 \times 10^{-5}$ in standard notation, move the decimal point 5 places to the left.
$8.9 \times 10^{-5} = 0.000089$

14. To write $4.41 \times 10^{-2}$ in standard notation, move the decimal point 2 places to the left.
$4.41 \times 10^{-2} = 0.0441$

15. $\left(7 \times 10^6\right) - \left(5.3 \times 10^6\right)$
$= (7 - 5.3) \times 10^6$
$= 1.7 \times 10^6$

16. $\left(3.4 \times 10^4\right) + \left(7.1 \times 10^5\right)$
$= \left(0.34 \times 10^5\right) + \left(7.1 \times 10^5\right)$
$= (0.34 \times 7.1) \times 10^5$
$= 7.44 \times 10^5$

17. $\left(2 \times 10^4\right)\left(5.4 \times 10^6\right)$
$= (2 \times 5.4)\left(10^4 \times 10^6\right)$
$= (10.8)\left(10^{4+6}\right)$
$= (10.8)\left(10^{10}\right)$
$= 1.08 \times 10^{11}$

18. $\dfrac{7.86 \times 10^9}{3 \times 10^4}$
$= \dfrac{7.86}{3} \times \dfrac{10^9}{10^4}$
$= 2.62 \times 10^5$

19. $\dfrac{4.503 \times 10^9}{5.791 \times 10^7}$
$= \dfrac{4.503}{5.791} \times \dfrac{10^9}{10^7}$
$= \dfrac{4.503}{5.791} \times 10^{9-7}$
$= 0.7776 \times 10^2$
$= 7.776 \times 10^1$

20. Sample answer: Very large numbers, such as distances in space, and very small numbers, such as the sizes of atomic particles, can be written in scientific notation.

# Solutions Key

## Proportional and Nonproportional Relationships and Functions

**MODULE 3** *Proportional Relationships*

**Are You Ready?**

1.
$$
\begin{array}{r}
0.375 \\
8\overline{)3.000} \\
-2\,400 \\
\hline
600 \\
-560 \\
\hline
40 \\
-40 \\
\hline
0
\end{array}
$$
0.375

2. $\dfrac{0.3}{0.4} = \dfrac{0.3 \times 10}{0.4 \times 10}$

$= \dfrac{3}{4}$

$$
\begin{array}{r}
0.75 \\
4\overline{)3.00} \\
-2\,80 \\
\hline
20 \\
-20 \\
\hline
0
\end{array}
$$
0.75

3. $\dfrac{0.13}{0.2} = \dfrac{0.13 \times 100}{0.2 \times 100}$

$= \dfrac{13}{20}$

$$
\begin{array}{r}
0.65 \\
20\overline{)13.00} \\
-12.00 \\
\hline
100 \\
-100 \\
\hline
0
\end{array}
$$
0.65

4. $\dfrac{0.39}{0.75} = \dfrac{0.39 \times 100}{0.75 \times 100}$

$= \dfrac{39}{75}$

$$
\begin{array}{r}
0.52 \\
75\overline{)39.00} \\
-37\,50 \\
\hline
150 \\
-150 \\
\hline
0
\end{array}
$$
0.52

5.
$$
\begin{array}{r}
0.8 \\
5\overline{)4.0} \\
-40 \\
\hline
0
\end{array}
$$
0.8

6.
$$
\begin{array}{r}
0.05 \\
2\overline{)0.10} \\
-10 \\
\hline
0
\end{array}
$$
0.05

7.
$$
\begin{array}{r}
0.25 \\
14\overline{)3.50} \\
-28 \\
\hline
70 \\
-70 \\
\hline
0
\end{array}
$$
0.25

8.
$$
\begin{array}{r}
0.5 \\
14\overline{)7.0} \\
-70 \\
\hline
0
\end{array}
$$
0.5

9.
$$
\begin{array}{r}
0.03 \\
10\overline{)0.30} \\
-30 \\
\hline
0
\end{array}
$$
0.03

10. $\dfrac{20}{18} = \dfrac{10}{x}$

$\dfrac{20 \div 2}{18 \div 2} = \dfrac{10}{x}$

$\dfrac{10}{9} = \dfrac{10}{x}$

$x = 9$

11. $\dfrac{x}{12} = \dfrac{30}{72}$

$\dfrac{x \times 6}{12 \times 6} = \dfrac{30}{72}$

$\dfrac{6x}{72} = \dfrac{30}{72}$

$6x = 30$

$x = 5$

12. $\dfrac{x}{4} = \dfrac{4}{16}$

$\dfrac{x \times 4}{4 \times 4} = \dfrac{4}{16}$

$\dfrac{4x}{16} = \dfrac{4}{16}$

$4x = 4$

$x = 1$

13. $\dfrac{11}{x} = \dfrac{132}{120}$

$\dfrac{11 \times 12}{x \times 12} = \dfrac{132}{120}$

$\dfrac{132}{12x} = \dfrac{132}{120}$

$12x = 120$

$x = 10$

14. $\dfrac{36}{48} = \dfrac{x}{4}$

$\dfrac{36 \div 12}{48 \div 12} = \dfrac{x}{4}$

$\dfrac{3}{4} = \dfrac{x}{4}$

$x = 3$

15. $\dfrac{x}{9} = \dfrac{21}{27}$

$\dfrac{x \times 3}{9 \times 3} = \dfrac{21}{27}$

$\dfrac{3x}{27} = \dfrac{21}{27}$

$3x = 21$

$x = 7$

16. $\dfrac{24}{16} = \dfrac{x}{2}$

$\dfrac{24 \div 8}{16 \div 8} = \dfrac{x}{2}$

$\dfrac{3}{2} = \dfrac{x}{2}$

$x = 3$

17. $\dfrac{30}{15} = \dfrac{6}{x}$

$\dfrac{30 \div 5}{15 \div 5} = \dfrac{6}{x}$

$\dfrac{6}{3} = \dfrac{6}{x}$

$x = 3$

18. $\dfrac{3}{x} = \dfrac{18}{36}$

$\dfrac{3}{x} = \dfrac{18 \div 6}{36 \div 6}$

$\dfrac{3}{x} = \dfrac{3}{6}$

$x = 6$

## LESSON 3.1

### Your Turn

3.

| Number of hours | 1 | 2 | 3 | 4 |
|---|---|---|---|---|
| Number of bicycles | 15 | 30 | 45 | 60 |

$\dfrac{15}{1} = 15, \dfrac{30}{2} = 15, \dfrac{45}{3} = 15, \dfrac{60}{4} = 15$

Let $x$ represent the number of hours.
Let $y$ represent the number of bicycles.
$y = 15x$

4. The point (5, 6) indicates that in 5 hours, the hiker hiked 6 miles.

5.

| Time (h) | 5 | 10 | 15 |
|---|---|---|---|
| Distance (mi) | 6 | 12 | 18 |

$\dfrac{6}{5}, \dfrac{12}{10} = \dfrac{6}{5}, \dfrac{18}{15} = \dfrac{6}{5}$

Let $x$ represent the number of hours.
Let $y$ represent the number of miles.

$y = \dfrac{6}{5}x$

### Guided Practice

1. A proportional relationship is a relationship between two quantities in which the ratio of one quantity to the other quantity is constant.

2. When writing an equation of a proportional relationship in the form $y = kx$, $k$ is replaced with the constant of proportionality.

3. a.

| Time (weeks) | 1 | 2 | 4 | 8 | 10 |
|---|---|---|---|---|---|
| Time (days) | 7 | 14 | 28 | 56 | 70 |

b. $\dfrac{7}{1} = 7, \dfrac{14}{2} = 7, \dfrac{28}{4} = 7, \dfrac{56}{8} = 7, \dfrac{70}{10} = 7$

Let $x$ represent the time in weeks.
Let $y$ represent the time in days.
The equation that describes the relationship is $y = 7x$.

4.

| Oxygen atoms | 2 | 5 | 17 | 120 |
|---|---|---|---|---|
| Hydrogen atoms | 4 | 10 | 34 | 240 |

$\dfrac{4}{2} = 2, \dfrac{10}{5} = 2, \dfrac{34}{17} = 2, \dfrac{240}{120} = 2$

Let $x$ represent the number of oxygen atoms.
Let $y$ represent the number of hydrogen atoms.
$y = 2x$.

5.

| Distance (in.) | 1 | 2 | 3 |
|---|---|---|---|
| Actual distance (mi) | 30 | 60 | 90 |

$\dfrac{30}{1} = 30, \dfrac{60}{2} = 30, \dfrac{90}{3} = 30$

Let $x$ represent the distance in inches.
Let $y$ represent the actual distance in miles.
$y = 30x$.

6. Sample answer: Use the equation to make a table with $x$-values and $y$-values. Then graph the points $(x, y)$ and draw a line through the points.

### Independent Practice

7. $\dfrac{50}{10} = 5, \dfrac{68}{20} = \dfrac{17}{5}$

No; the ratios of the numbers in each column are not equal.

8.

Sample answer: The graph is a line starting at (0, 32) and slanting upward to the right.

9. a. Sample answer: The account had a balance of $100 to begin with.

   b. Sample answer: Have Ralph open the account with no initial deposit and then put $20 in every month.

10. Sample answer:
   Let $x$ represent the number of nickels you have.
   Let $y$ represent the amount of money you have in dollars.

   $$y = \frac{1}{20}x$$

11. $$\frac{8}{20} = \frac{42}{y}$$
   $$8 \cdot y = 20 \cdot 42$$
   $$8y = 840$$
   $$\frac{8y}{8} = \frac{840}{8}$$
   $$y = 105$$

12. $$\frac{12}{8} = \frac{x}{12}$$
   $$12 \cdot 12 = 8 \cdot x$$
   $$144 = 8x$$
   $$\frac{144}{8} = \frac{8x}{8}$$
   $$18 = x$$

13. a.

| Distance (in.) | 10 | 20 | 30 | 40 | 50 |
|---|---|---|---|---|---|
| Time (min) | 1 | 2 | 3 | 4 | 5 |

   b. $\frac{1}{10}, \frac{2}{20} = \frac{1}{10}, \frac{3}{30} = \frac{1}{10}, \frac{4}{40} = \frac{1}{10}, \frac{5}{50} = \frac{1}{10}$

   Let $x$ represent the distance in inches.
   Let $y$ represent the time in minutes.

   $$y = \frac{1}{10}x$$

   c. $$y = \frac{1}{10}x$$
   $$y = \frac{1}{10}(85)$$
   $$y = 8.5$$
   It takes 8.5 minutes.

## Focus on Higher Order Thinking

14. Sample answer: All of the graphs represent real-world data for which both $x$ and $y$ take on only nonnegative values. When both coordinates are positive, the corresponding point will be in the first quadrant or on the axes. If either $x$ or $y$ or both could be negative, then other quadrants would be needed.

15.

| Length of side of square | 1 | 2 | 3 | 4 | 5 |
|---|---|---|---|---|---|
| Perimeter of square | 4 | 8 | 12 | 16 | 20 |
| Area of square | 1 | 4 | 9 | 16 | 25 |

a. $\frac{4}{1} = 4, \frac{8}{2} = 4, \frac{12}{3} = 4, \frac{16}{4} = 4, \frac{20}{5} = 4$

Yes. The ratio of the perimeter of a square to its side length is always 4.

b. $\frac{1}{1} = 1, \frac{4}{2} = 2$

No. The ratio of the area of a square to its side length is not constant.

16. The new constant of proportionality is the reciprocal of the original constant of proportionality.

## LESSON 3.2

### Your Turn

1. Find the rates of change.

   $$\frac{18 - 0}{0.5 - 0} = \frac{18}{0.5} = 36$$

   $$\frac{31 - 18}{1.5 - 0.5} = \frac{13}{1} = 13$$

   $$\frac{26 - 31}{2 - 1.5} = \frac{-5}{0.5} = -10$$

   The rates of change are variable.

4. Use points (4, 3) and (8, 6).
   rise $= +3$
   run $= +4$
   $$\frac{\text{rise}}{\text{run}} = \frac{3}{4}$$
   Rate of leaking $= \frac{3}{4}$ gallon(s) per minute

### Guided Practice

1. $$\frac{4 - 1}{12 - 3} = \frac{3}{9} = \frac{1}{3}$$

   $$\frac{9 - 4}{27 - 12} = \frac{5}{15} = \frac{1}{3}$$

   $$\frac{25 - 9}{75 - 27} = \frac{16}{48} = \frac{1}{3}$$

   The rates of change are constant.

2. $$\frac{12 - 6}{4 - 2} = \frac{6}{2} = 3$$

   $$\frac{25 - 12}{9 - 4} = \frac{13}{5}$$

   The rates of change are variable.

3. $$\frac{2 - 1}{64 - 16} = \frac{1}{48}$$

   $$\frac{3 - 2}{144 - 64} = \frac{1}{80}$$

   The rates of change are variable.

4. $$\frac{76 - 38}{4 - 2} = \frac{38}{2} = 19$$

   $$\frac{133 - 76}{7 - 4} = \frac{57}{3} = 19$$

   $$\frac{171 - 133}{9 - 7} = \frac{38}{2} = 19$$

   The rates of change are constant.

5. Use points (1, 200) and (2, 400).

   $$\frac{\text{change in distance}}{\text{change in time}} = \frac{400 - 200}{2 - 1}$$

   $$= \frac{200}{1} = 200 \text{ ft per min}$$

6. Use points $(1, 200)$ and $(4, 800)$.

$$\frac{\text{change in distance}}{\text{change in time}} = \frac{800 - 200}{4 - 1}$$

$$= \frac{600}{3} = 200 \text{ ft per min}$$

The rate of change is 200 ft per min.

7. Use points $(-1, 2)$ and $(1, -2)$.
rise $= -4$
run $= 2$
$$\frac{\text{rise}}{\text{run}} = \frac{-4}{2}$$
The slope is $-2$.

8. Use points $(-2, -3)$ and $(2, 3)$.
rise $= 6$
run $= 4$
$$\frac{\text{rise}}{\text{run}} = \frac{6}{4} = \frac{3}{2}$$

The slope is $\frac{3}{2}$.

9. Sample answer: Find the coordinates of two points on the line. Then divide the change in $y$-values (the rise) from one point to the other by the change in $x$-values (the run).

## Independent Practice

10. a. Slope of $\overline{EF} = \frac{\text{rise}}{\text{run}} = \frac{2 - 5}{6 - (-3)} = \frac{-3}{9} = -\frac{1}{3}$

Slope of $\overline{EF} = -\frac{1}{3}$

Slope of $\overline{FG} = \frac{\text{rise}}{\text{run}} = \frac{-4 - 2}{4 - 6} = \frac{-6}{-2} = 3$

Slope of $\overline{FG} = 3$

Slope of $\overline{GH} = \frac{\text{rise}}{\text{run}} = \frac{-1 - (-4)}{-5 - 4} = \frac{3}{-9} = -\frac{1}{3}$

Slope of $\overline{GH} = -\frac{1}{3}$

Slope of $\overline{HE} = \frac{\text{rise}}{\text{run}} = \frac{-1 - 5}{-5 - (-3)} = \frac{-6}{-2} = 3$

Slope of $\overline{HE} = 3$

b. The slopes of opposite sides are the same.

c. The slopes of adjacent sides are negative reciprocals of each other.

11. The total distance is 4.5 miles + 7.5 miles, or 12 miles.
The total amount of time is 48 minutes.

48 minutes $= \frac{48}{60}$ hour or 0.8 hour.

The average rate of speed $= \frac{12 \text{ mi}}{0.8 \text{ hr}} = 15$ mph.

12. Use the first two points to find the slope of the line.

slope $= \frac{\text{rise}}{\text{run}} = \frac{4 - 3}{8 - 6} = \frac{1}{2}$

The slope found using the second two points must

also be $\frac{1}{2}$.

$$\frac{-2 - 4}{n - 8} = \frac{1}{2}$$

$$\frac{-6}{n - 8} = \frac{1}{2}$$

$n - 8 = -12$
$n = -4$

13. a. The container lost 2 gallons of water in 10 minutes.

$$\frac{2 \text{ gal}}{10 \text{ min}} = 0.2 \text{ gal per min}$$

The water is leaking at a rate of 0.2 gal per min.

b. Solve the proportion $\frac{2 \text{ gal}}{10 \text{ min}} = \frac{5 \text{ gal}}{x \text{ min}}$.

$$\frac{2}{10} = \frac{5}{x}$$
$$2x = 50$$
$$x = 25$$
The container will be empty in 25 minutes.

14. He used the ratio of the change in $x$ over the change in $y$ instead of the ratio of the change in $y$ over the change in $x$.

15.

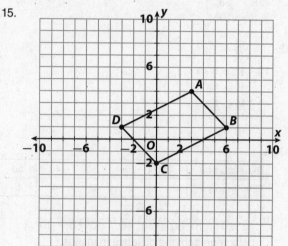

a. Slope of $\overline{AB} = \frac{\text{rise}}{\text{run}} = \frac{1 - 4}{6 - 3} = \frac{-3}{3} = -1$

Slope of $\overline{AB} = -1$

Slope of $\overline{BC} = \frac{\text{rise}}{\text{run}} = \frac{-2 - 1}{0 - 6} = \frac{-3}{-6} = \frac{1}{2}$

Slope of $\overline{BC} = \frac{1}{2}$

Slope of $\overline{CD} = \frac{\text{rise}}{\text{run}} = \frac{1 - (-2)}{-3 - 0} = \frac{3}{-3} = -1$

Slope of $\overline{CD} = -1$

Slope of $\overline{DA} = \frac{\text{rise}}{\text{run}} = \frac{1 - 4}{-3 - 3} = \frac{-3}{-6} = \frac{1}{2}$

Slope of $\overline{DA} = \frac{1}{2}$

b. The slopes of opposite sides are the same.

c. Yes. The slopes of opposite sides are always the same.

## Focus on Higher Order Thinking

16. Yes. The slope of a line is constant. Therefore, the calculated slope will be the same no matter which two points are chosen.

17. Sample answer: The lines are equally steep, but the one with the positive slope slants upward from left to right and the one with the negative slope slants downward from left to right.

18. The slope of the x-axis is 0.
Sample answer: The rise along the x-axis is zero, while the run along the x-axis is not zero. The slope is $\frac{\text{zero}}{\text{run}}$ or zero.

## LESSON 3.3

### Your Turn

2.

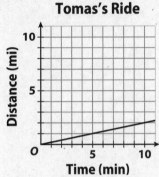

**Tomas's Ride**

Slope $= \frac{\text{rise}}{\text{run}} = \frac{1}{5}$, so the unit rate is $\frac{1}{5}$.

His rate of speed is $\frac{1}{5}$ mi/min.

4. The slope of the graph of $y = 375x$ is 375.
Therefore Plane A's rate of speed is 375 mph.
The graph for Plane B contains the point (1, 425), so the slope of the graph is 425. Therefore, Plane B's rate of speed is 425 mph.
Plane B is flying at a faster rate of speed.

### Guided Practice

1. Use the points (0, 0) and (12, 10).
Slope $= \frac{\text{rise}}{\text{run}} = \frac{10}{12} = \frac{5}{6}$, so the unit rate is $\frac{5}{6}$ mi/hr.

2. Use the points (4, 5) and (8, 10).
Slope $= \frac{\text{rise}}{\text{run}} = \frac{5}{4}$, so the unit rate is $\frac{5}{4}$ mi/hr.

3. The slope of the graph of $y = 0.5x$ is 0.5, so Henry's rate is 0.5 mph.
Use the point (4, 6) to find the slope of the graph given for Clark's hike.
Slope $= \frac{\text{rise}}{\text{run}} = \frac{6}{4} = \frac{3}{2} = 1.5$

So Clark's rate is 1.5 mph.
Therefore, Clark is faster.

4. $\frac{15}{1} = \frac{30}{2} = \frac{45}{3} = \frac{60}{4} = \frac{90}{6} = 15$
$y = 15x$

5. $\frac{6}{16} = \frac{12}{32} = \frac{18}{48} = \frac{24}{64} = \frac{3}{8}$
$y = \frac{3}{8}x$

6. Sample answer: Table of values: The ratio of y to x gives the unit rate and the slope. Equation: If the equation can be written as $y = mx$, then m is the unit rate and the slope. Graph: When the line passes through the origin, then the value of r at the point (1, r) is the unit rate and the slope.

### Independent Practice

7. a.

| Time (min) | 4 | 8 | 12 | 16 | 20 |
|------------|---|---|----|----|----|
| Distance (mi) | 3 | 6 | 9 | 12 | 15 |

b.

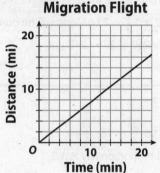

**Migration Flight**

c. Use the point (8, 6).
Slope $= \frac{\text{rise}}{\text{run}} = \frac{6}{8} = \frac{3}{4}$

The slope is $\frac{3}{4}$, which means that the unit rate of migration is $\frac{3}{4}$ mi/min.

8. A unit rate is a rate in which the second quantity in the comparison is one unit.

9. a. Machine 1: slope $=$ unit rate $= \frac{0.6}{1} = 0.6$ gal/s

For Machine 2, use the point (8, 6).
Slope $= \frac{\text{rise}}{\text{run}} = \frac{6}{8} = \frac{3}{4}$
Machine 2: slope $=$ unit rate $= \frac{3}{4} = 0.75$ gal/s

b. Since $0.75 > 0.6$, Machine 2 is working at a faster rate.

10. In the equation $y = \frac{1}{9}x$, $\frac{1}{9}$ is the slope, so Patrick's rate is $\frac{1}{9}$ kilometer per minute. Jennifer's rate is $\frac{5}{40}$ or $\frac{1}{8}$ kilometer per minute. Since $\frac{1}{8} > \frac{1}{9}$, Jennifer has the faster training rate.

### Focus on Higher Order Thinking

11. The slope and the unit rate are both 4.75; If the graph of a proportional relationship passes through the point (1, r), then r equals the slope and the unit rate, which is $4.75/min.

12. Car B is traveling at the faster rate; The slope of the graph is equal to the unit rate of speed.

Car A: slope $= \dfrac{27.5 - 0}{0.5 - 0} = \dfrac{27.5}{0.5} = 55$ mph

Car B: slope $= \dfrac{240 - 0}{4 - 0} = \dfrac{240}{4} = 60$ mph

$60 > 55$, so Car B is traveling faster.

13. After $13\frac{1}{2}$ minutes, 243 gallons will have been pumped into the pool; Sample answer: The unit rate is $\dfrac{36}{2} = 18$ gal/min. So $1\frac{1}{2}$ minutes after 12 minutes, an additional $18 \times 1\frac{1}{2} = 27$ gallons will be pumped in, so the total is $216 + 27 = 243$ gal.

# MODULE 3

## Ready to Go On?

1. $\dfrac{3}{2} = 1.5$, $\dfrac{4.5}{3} = 1.5$, $\dfrac{6}{4} = 1.5$, $\dfrac{7.5}{5} = 1.5$

The constant of proportionality is 1.5.

2. $\dfrac{25}{2} = 12.5$, $\dfrac{37.5}{3} = 12.5$, $\dfrac{50}{4} = 12.5$

The constant of proportionality $k$ is 12.5.
The equation is $y = 12.5x$.

3. Use $(0, 0)$ and $(1, 3)$.

$\dfrac{\text{rise}}{\text{run}} = \dfrac{3}{1}$

The slope is 3.

4. Use $(0, 0)$ and $(1, -5)$.

$\dfrac{\text{rise}}{\text{run}} = \dfrac{-5}{1}$

The slope is $-5$.

5.  Train A              Train B

$\dfrac{2}{140} = 70$        $\dfrac{2}{150} = 75$

Train A has a rate of 70 km per hour; Train B has a rate of 75 km per hour. Train B is faster.

6. Sample answer: The graph of a proportional relationship is a line that passes through the origin. The slope of the line is the unit rate of change.

# MODULE 4 *Nonproportional Relationships*

## Are You Ready?

1. $3 - (-5)$
   $3 + 5$
   $8$

2. $-4 - 5$
   $-9$

3. $6 - 10$
   $-4$

4. $-5 - (-3)$
   $-5 + 3$
   $-2$

5. $8 - (-8)$
   $8 + 8$
   $16$

6. $9 - 5$
   $4$

7. $-3 - 9$
   $-12$

8. $0 - (-6)$
   $0 + 6$
   $6$

9. $12 - (-9)$
   $12 + 9$
   $21$

10. $-6 - (-4)$
    $-6 + 4$
    $-2$

11. $-7 - 10$
    $-17$

12. $5 - 14$
    $-9$

13–16.

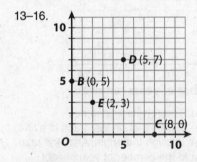

## LESSON 4.1

### Your Turn

1. Sample answer:
   $y = 12x - 4$     $y = 12x - 4$
   $y = 12(2) - 4$   $y = 12(3) - 4$
   $y = 20$        $y = 32$

---

$y = 12x - 4$     $y = 12x - 4$
$y = 12(4) - 4$   $y = 12(5) - 4$
$y = 44$        $y = 56$

| x (number of hours) | 2 | 3 | 4 | 5 |
|---|---|---|---|---|
| y (earnings in dollars) | 20 | 32 | 44 | 56 |

3. $y = -2x + 1$     $y = -2x + 1$
   $y = -2(-1) + 1$   $y = -2(0) + 1$
   $y = 3$        $y = 1$

   $y = -2x + 1$     $y = -2x + 1$
   $y = -2(1) + 1$   $y = -2(2) + 1$
   $y = -1$       $y = -3$

| x | −1 | 0 | 1 | 2 |
|---|---|---|---|---|
| y | 3 | 1 | −1 | −3 |

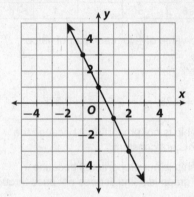

### Guided Practice

1. $y = 2x + 5$     $y = 2x + 5$
   $y = 2(-2) + 5$   $y = 2(-1) + 5$
   $y = 1$        $y = 3$

   $y = 2x + 5$     $y = 2x + 5$
   $y = 2(0) + 5$   $y = 2(1) + 5$
   $y = 5$        $y = 7$

   $y = 2x + 5$
   $y = 2(2) + 5$
   $y = 9$

| x | −2 | −1 | 0 | 1 | 2 |
|---|---|---|---|---|---|
| y | 1 | 3 | 5 | 7 | 9 |

2. $y = \frac{3}{8}x - 5$          $y = \frac{3}{8}x - 5$

$y = \frac{3}{8}(-8) - 5$      $y = \frac{3}{8}(0) - 5$

$y = -8$             $y = -5$

$y = \frac{3}{8}x - 5$          $y = \frac{3}{8}x - 5$

$y = \frac{3}{8}(8) - 5$       $y = \frac{3}{8}(16) - 5$

$y = -2$             $y = 1$

$y = \frac{3}{8}x - 5$

$y = \frac{3}{8}(24) - 5$

$y = 4$

| x | −8 | 0 | 8 | 16 | 24 |
|---|----|---|---|----|----|
| y | −8 | −5 | −2 | 1 | 4 |

3. Calculate the value of $\frac{y}{x}$ for each pair of values.

$\frac{3}{0}$ is undefined.

$\frac{7}{2} = 3.5,\ \frac{11}{4} = 2.75,\ \frac{15}{6} = 2.5,\ \frac{19}{8} = 2.375$

The relationship is not proportional because the ratio of $y$ to $x$ is not constant.

4. The relationship is not proportional because although the graph is a line, it does not pass through the origin.

5. $y = x - 1$          $y = x - 1$
   $y = (-2) - 1$     $y = (-1) - 1$
   $y = -3$          $y = -2$

   $y = x - 1$          $y = x - 1$
   $y = (0) - 1$       $y = (1) - 1$
   $y = -1$          $y = 0$

   $y = x - 1$
   $y = (2) - 1$
   $y = 1$

| x | −2 | −1 | 0 | 1 | 2 |
|---|----|----|---|---|---|
| y | −3 | −2 | −1 | 0 | 1 |

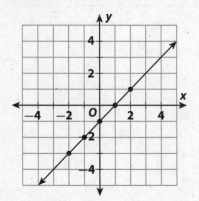

6. Sample answer: Choose values that make sense in the context. For example, the number of games played must be a whole number.

**Independent Practice**

7. The graph is a set of unconnected points; Sample answer: The values of $x$ must be whole numbers, since you cannot buy a fractional part of a lunch.

8. The graph is a solid line; Sample answer: The values of $x$ can be any number, since the distance remaining can be measured at any moment in time.

9. a. Sample answer:

   $y = 8x + 12$         $y = 8x + 12$
   $y = 8(0) + 12$      $y = 8(1) + 12$
   $y = 12$           $y = 20$

   $y = 8x + 12$         $y = 8x + 12$
   $y = 8(2) + 12$      $y = 8(3) + 12$
   $y = 28$           $y = 36$

   $y = 8x + 12$
   $y = 8(4) + 12$
   $y = 44$

| x (number of years renewed) | 0 | 1 | 2 | 3 | 4 |
|---|---|---|---|---|---|
| y (total cost in dollars) | 12 | 20 | 28 | 36 | 44 |

b.

**Magazine Subscription Costs**

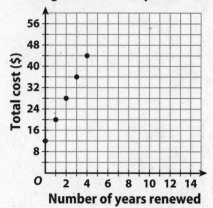

c. Sample answer: The relationship is not proportional because although the graph is a line, it does not pass through the origin. Also, the ratio of the total cost to the number of years is not constant.

d. No; The graph is a set of unconnected points because the values of $x$ represent whole numbers of years.

10. Sample answer: In a proportional relationship, the ratio of each $y$-value to its corresponding $x$-value must be constant. In addition, its graph must be a line that passes through the origin.

11. Sample answer: In a table, the ratios of each $y$-value to its corresponding $x$-value will not be equal. The graph will not pass through the origin. The equation can be written in the form $y = mx + b$, with $b \neq 0$.

## Focus on Higher Order Thinking

12. Sample answer: George's observation is true, but his claim is false. There is a constant rate of change. However, the relationship is not proportional because the ratio of $y$ to $x$ (90, 75, 70, 67.5, 66) is not constant.

13. At most one; Sample answer: A line representing a proportional relationship must pass through the origin. A line parallel to it cannot also pass through the origin, so at most one of the lines can represent a proportional relationship.

## LESSON 4.2

### Your Turn

1. Use the points (2, 22) and (4, 32) to find the slope.

$$m = \frac{32 - 22}{4 - 2} = \frac{10}{2} = 5$$

The slope $m$ is 5.
The difference between the $x$-values is 2. The difference between the $y$-values is 10. Working backward, when $x = 0$, $y = 12$. The $y$-intercept $b$ is 12.

2. Use the points (1, 8) and (2, 15) to find the slope.

$$m = \frac{15 - 8}{2 - 1} = \frac{7}{1} = 7$$

The slope $m$ is 7.
The difference between the $x$-values is 1. The difference between the $y$-values is 7. Working backward, when $x = 0$, $y = 1$. The $y$-intercept $b$ is 1.

### Guided Practice

1. Use the points (0, 1) and (2, −3) to find the slope.

$$m = \frac{-3 - 1}{2 - 0} = \frac{-4}{2} = -2$$

The slope is −2.
The $y$-intercept is 1, since 1 is the $y$-coordinate of the point where the graph intersects the $y$-axis.
slope $m = -2$
$y$-intercept $b = 1$

2. Use the points (0, −15) and (3, 0) to find the slope.

$$m = \frac{0 - (-15)}{3 - 0} = \frac{15}{3} = 5$$

The slope is 5.
The $y$-intercept is −15, since −15 is the $y$-coordinate of the point where the graph intersects the $y$-axis.
slope $m = 5$
$y$-intercept $b = -15$

3. Use the points (0, −2) and (2, 1) to find the slope.

$$m = \frac{1 - (-2)}{2 - 0} = \frac{3}{2}$$

The slope is $\frac{3}{2}$.
The $y$-intercept is −2, since −2 is the $y$-coordinate of the point where the graph intersects the $y$-axis.
slope $m = \frac{3}{2}$
$y$-intercept $b = -2$

4. Use the points (0, 9) and (3, 0) to find the slope.

$$m = \frac{0 - 9}{3 - 0} = \frac{-9}{3} = -3$$

The slope is −3.
The $y$-intercept is 9, since 9 is the $y$-coordinate of the point where the graph intersects the $y$-axis.
slope $m = -3$
$y$-intercept $b = 9$

5. Use the points (2, 7) and (4, 13) to find the slope.

$$m = \frac{13 - 7}{4 - 2} = \frac{6}{2} = 3$$

The slope is 3.
The difference between the $x$-values is 2. The difference between the $y$-values is 6. Working backward, when $x = 0$, $y = 1$. The $y$-intercept is 1.
slope $m = 3$
$y$-intercept $b = 1$

6. Use the points (5, 120) and (10, 100) to find the slope.

$$m = \frac{100 - 120}{10 - 5} = \frac{-20}{5} = -4$$

The slope is −4.
The difference between the $x$-values is 5. The difference between the $y$-values is −20. Working backward, when $x = 0$, $y = 140$. The $y$-intercept is 140.
slope $m = -4$
$y$-intercept $b = 140$

7. Find the slope by substituting the coordinates of two points on the line into the slope formula. Find the $y$-intercept by identifying the $y$-coordinate of the point where the graph crosses the $y$-axis.

### Independent Practice

8. Use the points (1, 125) and (2, 175) to find the rate of change.

$$\text{rate of change} = \frac{175 - 125}{2 - 1} = \frac{50}{1} = 50$$

The rate of change is $50 per room.
The difference between the $x$-values is 1. The difference between the $y$-values is 50. Working backward, when $x = 0$, $y = 75$.
The initial value is $75, which represents a flat fee no matter how many rooms are cleaned.

9. a. Use the points (1, 17) and (2, 29) to find the hourly rate.

$$\text{hourly rate} = \frac{29 - 17}{2 - 1} = \frac{12}{1} = 12$$

The rate to rent a paddleboat is $12 per hour. To find the cost to park for a day, find the initial value. The difference between the $x$-values is 1. The difference between the $y$-values is 12. Working backward, when $x = 0$, $y = 5$.
It costs $5 to park for the day.

b. 3.5 hours × $12 per hour + $5 = $47
$47 ÷ 2 = $23.50
Lin will pay $23.50.

10. a. Use the points $(1, 55)$ and $(2, 85)$ to find the rate of change.

rate of change $= \frac{85 - 55}{2 - 1} = \frac{30}{1} = 30$

The rate of change is $30 per lesson.
The difference between the $x$-values is 1. The difference between the $y$-values is 30. Working backward, when $x = 0$, $y = 25$.
The initial value is $25.

b. Use the points $(1, 75)$ and $(2, 125)$ to find the rate of change.

rate of change $= \frac{125 - 75}{2 - 1} = \frac{50}{1} = 50$

The rate of change is $50 per lesson.
The difference between the $x$-values is 1. The difference between the $y$-values is 50. Working backward, when $x = 0$, $y = 25$.
The initial value is $25.

c. Both rates of change are constant, but the private lessons cost more. There is a flat fee of $25 no matter which type of lessons Raymond takes.

11. Find the rates of change.

$\frac{6.5 - 4.5}{2 - 1} = \frac{2}{1} = 2$

$\frac{8.5 - 6.5}{3 - 2} = \frac{2}{1} = 2$

$\frac{11.5 - 8.5}{4 - 3} = \frac{3}{1} = 3$

The rate of change is not constant.

12. Find the rates of change.

$\frac{126 - 140}{5 - 3} = \frac{-14}{2} = -7$

$\frac{110 - 126}{7 - 5} = \frac{-16}{2} = -8$

$\frac{92 - 110}{9 - 7} = \frac{-18}{2} = -9$

The rate of change is not constant.

## Focus on Higher Order Thinking

13. Substitute a random point $(x, y)$ and the point where the line crosses the $y$-axis, $(0, b)$, into the slope formula. Then solve the equation for $y$.

14. a. The slope is positive, so the amount should be increasing, not decreasing.
    b. Sample answer: I opened a savings account with $100 of birthday money, and I add $5 from my allowance every month.

15. John earns more from fees after parking 61 cars; He earns a fixed weekly salary of $300, plus $5 for each car he parks. He earns the same in fees as his fixed salary for parking $300 \div 5 = 60$ cars.

## LESSON 4.3

### Your Turn

2. Since $b = 1$, plot the point $(0, 1)$. Since $m = \frac{1}{2}$,

count up 1 and right 2 to plot a second point on the line, $(2, 2)$. Then draw a line through the points.

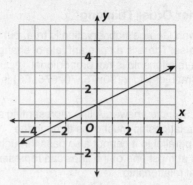

3. Since $b = 4$, plot the point $(0, 4)$. Since

$m = -3 = \frac{-3}{1}$, count down 3 and right 1 to plot

a second point on the line, $(1, 1)$. Then draw a line through the points.

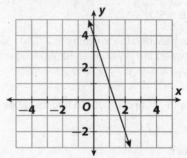

4. Since $b = 2400$, plot the point $(0, 2400)$. Since

$m = -200 = \frac{-200}{1}$, count down 200 and right 1

to plot a second point on the line, $(1, 2200)$. Then draw a line through the points.

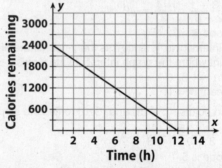

5. The new graph has the same $y$-intercept but a slope of $-200$ instead of $-300$, so it is less steep. It intersects the $x$-axis at $(12, 0)$ instead of $(8, 0)$.

6. The calories left to burn will decrease more slowly with each hour of exercise, so it will take longer for Ken to meet his goal.

7. Sample answer: The $y$-intercept would not change, but the slope would become $-600$, which would make the graph steeper. The line would intersect the $x$-axis at $(4, 0)$.

### Guided Practice

1. slope $= \frac{1}{2}$

   $y$-intercept $= -3$

Since $b = -3$, plot the point $(0, -3)$. Since $m = \frac{1}{2}$, count up 1 and right 2 to plot a second point on the line, $(2, -2)$. Then draw a line through the points.

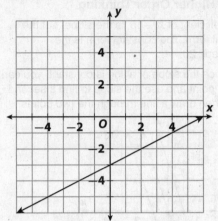

2. slope $= -3$
   $y$-intercept $= 2$
   Since $b = 2$, plot the point $(0, 2)$. Since
   $m = -3 = \frac{-3}{1}$, count down 3 and right 1 to plot a second point on the line, $(1, -1)$. Then draw a line through the points.

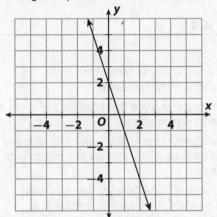

3. a. The slope is 4, indicating that you buy 4 cards each week. The $y$-intercept is 2, indicating that that was the number of cards you started with.

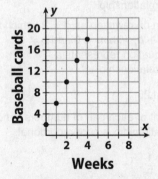

**Weeks**

   b. The points with coordinates that are not whole numbers do not make sense. You are buying only whole numbers of baseball cards and you are buying only once a week; See graph in part a above for additional plotted points.

4. Sample answer: You can easily identify the slope, $m$, and $y$-intercept, $b$, from the slope-intercept form $y = mx + b$ and quickly use them to locate two points that determine the line.

**Independent Practice**

5. a. Since $b = 0.25$, plot the point $(0, 0.25)$. Since $m = 0.75 = \frac{3}{4}$, count up 3 and right 4 to plot a second point on the line, $(1, 1)$. Then draw a line through the points.

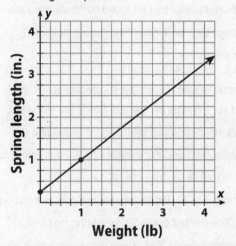

**Weight (lb)**

   b. The slope, 0.75, means that the spring stretches by 0.75 inch with each additional pound of weight. The $y$-intercept, 0.25, is the unstretched length of the spring in inches.

   c. The graph contains the point $(2, 1.75)$ indicating that if a 2-pound weight is hung on the spring, the spring will be 1.75 inches long; No; A 4-pound weight will stretch the spring to 3.25 inches, not 3.5 inches.

6. Sample answer: Since the $y$-intercept is $-1$, the point $(0, -1)$ lies on the line. Since the slope is 5, which is $\frac{5}{1}$, additional points can be found by increasing the $y$-values by 5 and the $x$-values by 1.
   Four points are:
   $(0, -1), (1, 4), (2, 9), (3, 14)$

7. Sample answer: Since the $y$-intercept is 8, the point $(0, 8)$ lies on the line. Since the slope is $-1$, which is $\frac{-1}{1}$, additional points can be found by decreasing the $y$-values by 1 and increasing the $x$-values by 1.
   Four points are:
   $(0, 8), (1, 7), (2, 6), (3, 5)$

8. Sample answer: Since the $y$-intercept is 0.3, the point $(0, 0.3)$ lies on the line. Since the slope is 0.2, which is $\frac{0.2}{1}$, additional points can be found by increasing the $y$-values by 0.2 and the $x$-values by 1.
   Four points are:
   $(0, 0.3), (1, 0.5), (2, 0.7), (3, 0.9)$

27

9. Sample answer: Since the $y$-intercept is $-3$, the point $(0, -3)$ lies on the line. Since the slope is 1.5, which is $\frac{1.5}{1}$, additional points can be found by increasing the $y$-values by 1.5 and the $x$-values by 1.
Four points are:
$(0, -3), (1, -1.5), (2, 0), (3, 1.5)$

10. Sample answer: Since the $y$-intercept is 4, the point $(0, 4)$ lies on the line. Since the slope is $-\frac{1}{2}$, additional points can be found by decreasing the $y$-values by 1 and increasing the $x$-values by 2.
Four points are:
$(0, 4), (2, 3), (4, 2), (6, 1)$

11. Sample answer: Since the $y$-intercept is $-5$, the point $(0, -5)$ lies on the line. Since the slope is $\frac{2}{3}$, additional points can be found by increasing the $y$-values by 2 and the $x$-values by 3. Four points are:
$(0, -5), (3, -3), (6, -1), (9, 1)$

12. The slope is 40, indicating that the cost per lesson is $40. The $y$-intercept is 30, indicating that that registration fee is $30. Since the $y$-intercept is 30, the point $(0, 30)$ lies on the line. Since the slope is 40, which is $\frac{40}{1}$, additional points can be found by increasing the $y$-values by 40 and the $x$-values by 1.
Four points are:
$(0, 30), (1, 70), (2, 110), (3, 150)$

13. a. Yes; Since the horizontal and vertical gridlines each represent 25 units, moving up 3 gridlines and right 1 gridline represents a slope of $\frac{75}{25}$, or 3.

b. Since $b = 50$, plot the point $(0, 50)$. Since $m = 3$, count up 3 and right 1 to plot a second point on the line, $(25, 125)$. Then draw a line through the points.

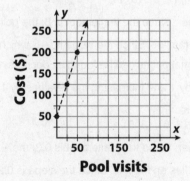

**Pool visits**

The slope is 3, which represents the charge per visit. The $y$-intercept is 50, which indicates that the membership fee is $50.

c. The graph shows that when $y = 200$, the value of $x$ is 50. Therefore, a member can get 50 visits for $200.

**Focus on Higher Order Thinking**

14. The coefficient of $x$, $-15$, is the slope, not the constant term. The constant term is the $y$-intercept, 20.

15. Yes; Since the slope of a line is constant, you can plot the point and use the slope to find a second point. Then draw a line through the two points.

16.

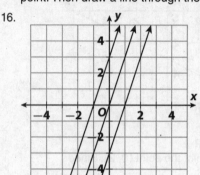

The lines are parallel. Parallel lines have the same slope but different $y$-intercepts.

## LESSON 4.4

**Your Turn**

1. Since the line does not contain the origin, the relationship is nonproportional.

2. Since the graph is a line that contains the origin, the relationship is proportional.

5. The equation is in the form $y = mx + b$, with $b = 0$. Therefore, the equation represents a proportional relationship.

6. The equation is in the form $y = mx + b$, with $b \neq 0$. Therefore, the equation represents a nonproportional relationship.

7. The equation can be rewritten as $n = -3p + 450$, which is in the form $y = mx + b$, with $b \neq 0$. Therefore, the equation represents a nonproportional relationship.

8. The equation can be rewritten as $d = 3$, which is in the form $y = mx + b$, with $m = 0$ and $b \neq 0$. Therefore, the equation represents a nonproportional relationship.

9. $\frac{30}{2} = 15$, $\frac{90}{8} = 11.25$
Since the quotient of each pair of numbers is not constant, the relationship is nonproportional.

10. $\frac{1}{5}$, $\frac{8}{40} = \frac{1}{5}$, $\frac{13}{65} = \frac{1}{5}$
Since the quotient of each pair of numbers is constant, the relationship is proportional.

11. Test-Prep Center A is cheaper for less than 20 hours; Test-Prep Center B is cheaper for more than 20 hours.

## Guided Practice

1. Since the graph is a line that contains the origin, the relationship is proportional.

2. Since the line does not contain the origin, the relationship is nonproportional.

3. The equation is in the form $y = mx + b$, with $b \neq 0$. Therefore, the equation represents a nonproportional relationship.

4. The equation is in the form $y = mx + b$, with $b = 0$. Therefore, the equation represents a proportional relationship.

5. $\frac{12}{3} = 4$, $\frac{36}{9} = 4$, $\frac{84}{21} = 4$

   Since the quotient of each pair of numbers is constant, the relationship is proportional.

6. $\frac{4}{22} = \frac{2}{11}$, $\frac{8}{46} = \frac{4}{23}$

   Since the ratio of each pair of numbers is not constant, the relationship is nonproportional.

7. Sample answer:

   $$\frac{12}{15,000,000} = 0.0000008$$

   $$\frac{16}{20,000,000} = 0.0000008$$

   $$\frac{20}{25,000,000} = 0.0000008$$

   The TV show rating is proportional to the number of households that watched, because the quotient when you divide the rating by the number of households is always 0.0000008.

8. Sample answer: Proportional relationships exist if the $y$-intercepts for a graph and an equation are 0, and if the table has, or would have, a value of 0 for $y$ when $x$ is 0.

## Independent Practice

9. a. Since the line does not contain the origin, the relationship is nonproportional.

   b. Use the points (0, 10) and (4, 12).

   $$m = \frac{12 - 10}{4 - 0} = \frac{2}{4} = \frac{1}{2}$$

   The slope is $\frac{1}{2}$, indicating that each cup of sports drink weighs $\frac{1}{2}$ pound. The $y$-intercept is 10, indicating that the empty cooler weighs 10 pounds.

10. Nonproportional; Sample answer: A graph of this situation would contain the point (0, 10), not the origin.

11. Proportional; The equation is in the form $y = mx + b$, with $b = 0$. Therefore, the equation represents a proportional relationship.

12. Both graphs contain the origin, but only Graph A is a line. Therefore, Graph A represents a proportional relationship, and Graph B represents a nonlinear, nonproportional relationship.

13. Sample answer: Amanda buys a flute for $500 and then pays $35 per week for lessons.

14. You can plot the point, use the slope to find another point, and draw a line through the points to see if the line passes through the origin. If it does, the relationship is proportional.

## Focus on Higher Order Thinking

15. a. No; using Equation B you see that the $y$-intercept is 273.15, not 0, so the graph does not contain the origin. Using Table C you see that the quotient of $K$ and $C$ is not constant: about 35.1, 19.21, and 8.5875.

    b. No; Equation A is in the form $y = mx + b$, with $F$ being used instead of $y$ and $C$ being used instead of $x$. The value of $b$ is 32. Since $b$ is not 0, the relationship is not proportional.

## MODULE 4

### Ready to Go On?

1. 
| $y = 3x + 2$ | $y = 3x + 2$ |
|---|---|
| $y = 3(-1) + 2$ | $y = 3(0) + 2$ |
| $y = -1$ | $y = 2$ |

| $y = 3x + 2$ | $y = 3x + 2$ |
|---|---|
| $y = 3(1) + 2$ | $y = 3(2) + 2$ |
| $y = 5$ | $y = 8$ |

$y = 3x + 5$
$y = 3(3) + 2$
$y = 11$

| x | −1 | 0 | 1 | 2 | 3 |
|---|---|---|---|---|---|
| y | −1 | 2 | 5 | 8 | 11 |

2. Use the points (0, 1) and (1, 4) to find the slope.

   $$m = \frac{4 - 1}{1 - 0} = \frac{3}{1} = 3$$

   The slope is 3.
   Since 1 is the $y$-coordinate of the point where the graph intersects the $y$-axis, the $y$-intercept is 1.

3. Since $b = -3$, plot the point $(0, -3)$. Since $m = 2 = \frac{2}{1}$, count up 2 and right 1 to plot a second point on the line, $(1, -1)$. Then draw a line through the points.

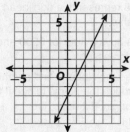

4. $\frac{4}{1} = 4, \frac{8}{2} = 4$

   Since the quotient of each pair of numbers is constant, the relationship is proportional.

5. The line includes the points $(1, 4)$ and $(-2, 5)$.

   $\frac{4}{1} = 4, \frac{5}{-2} = -2.5$

   Since the quotient of each pair of numbers is not constant, the relationship is nonproportional.

6. The line includes the points $(1, -1)$ and $(2, 1)$.

   $\frac{-1}{1} = -1, \frac{1}{2} = 0.5$

   Since the quotient of each pair of numbers is not constant, the relationship is nonproportional.

7. Table: for an ordered pair $(0, y)$, $y$ will not be 0; graph: the $y$-intercept will not be 0; equation: it will have the form $y = mx + b$ where $b \neq 0$.

## MODULE 5 *Writing Linear Equations*

### Are You Ready?

1.
$$
\begin{array}{r}
0.375 \\
8\overline{)3.000} \\
\underline{-2\,400} \\
600 \\
\underline{-560} \\
40 \\
\underline{-40} \\
0
\end{array}
$$
0.375

2. $\dfrac{0.3 \times 10}{0.4 \times 10} = \dfrac{3}{4}$
$$
\begin{array}{r}
0.75 \\
4\overline{)3.00} \\
\underline{-2\,80} \\
20 \\
\underline{-20} \\
0
\end{array}
$$
0.75

3. $\dfrac{0.13 \times 100}{0.2 \times 100} = \dfrac{13}{20}$
$$
\begin{array}{r}
0.65 \\
20\overline{)13.00} \\
\underline{-12.00} \\
100 \\
\underline{-100} \\
0
\end{array}
$$
0.65

4. $\dfrac{0.39 \times 100}{0.75 \times 100} = \dfrac{39}{75}$
$$
\begin{array}{r}
0.52 \\
75\overline{)39.00} \\
\underline{-37\,50} \\
150 \\
\underline{-150} \\
0
\end{array}
$$
0.52

5. $7p = 28$
$\dfrac{7p}{7} = \dfrac{28}{7}$
$p = 4$

6. $h - 13 = 5$
$\underline{+13 = +13}$
$h = 18$

7. $\dfrac{y}{3} = -6$
$\dfrac{y}{{}_{1}\cancel{3}}(\cancel{3}^{1}) = -6(3)$
$y = -18$

8. $b + 9 = 21$
$\underline{-9 = -9}$
$b = 12$

9. $c - 8 = -8$
$\underline{+8 = +8}$
$c = 0$

10. $3n = -12$
$\dfrac{3n}{3} = \dfrac{-12}{3}$
$n = -4$

11. $-16 = m + 7$
$\underline{-7 = \quad -7}$
$-23 = m$

12. $\dfrac{t}{-5} = -5$
$\dfrac{t}{{}_{1}\cancel{-5}}(\cancel{-5}^{1}) = -5\,(-5)$
$t = 25$

### LESSON 5.1

**Your Turn**

3. Use (0, 25) and (10, 0) to find the slope.
$$m = \frac{0 - 25}{10 - 0} = \frac{-25}{10} = -2.5$$

Read the *y*-intercept from the graph.
$b = 25$
Substitute into $y = mx + b$.
$y = -2.5x + 25$

5. Use (12, 16) and (8, 14) to find the slope.
$$m = \frac{14 - 16}{8 - 12} = \frac{-2}{-4} = 0.5$$

Use the slope and one of the ordered pairs,
(12, 16), to find *b*.
$y = mx + b$
$16 = 0.5(12) + b$
$16 = 6 + b$
$10 = b$
Substitute into $y = mx + b$.
$y = 0.5x + 10$

**Guided Practice**

1. a. The input variable is the length of the necklace in inches.

   b. The output variable is the total number of beads in the necklace.

   c. $y = 5x + 27$

2. Use (0, 300) and (5, 0) to find the slope.
$$m = \frac{0 - 300}{5 - 0} = \frac{-300}{5} = -60$$

Read the *y*-intercept from the graph.
$b = 300$
Substitute into $y = mx + b$.
$y = -60x + 300$

3. The input variable is the temperature in degrees Fahrenheit.
   The output variable is the number of chirps per minute.
   Use (59, 76) and (65, 100) to find the slope.

   $m = \dfrac{100 - 76}{65 - 59} = \dfrac{24}{6} = 4$

   Use the slope and (65, 100) to find $b$.

   $y = mx + b$
   $100 = 4(65) + b$
   $100 = 260 + b$
   $-160 = b$
   Substitute into $y = mx + b$.
   $y = 4x - 160$

4. The slope of the line is $m$, and the $y$-intercept is $b$.

## Independent Practice

5. If $x$ represents the number of seconds and $y$ represents the number of times the dragonfly beats its wings, then the equation is $y = 30x$.

6. If $x$ represents the number of seconds and $y$ represents the height of the balloon, then the equation is $y = 4x + 50$.

7. Use (0, −10) and (80, 0) to find the slope.

   $m = \dfrac{0 - (-10)}{80 - 0} = \dfrac{10}{80} = 0.125$

   The slope is 0.125, which indicates that the diver ascends at a rate of 0.125 m/s.

8. Read the $y$-intercept from the graph.
   $b = -10$
   The $y$-intercept is −10, which indicates that the diver starts 10 meters below the surface of the water.

9. $y = 0.125x - 10$

10. Use (0, 32) and (100, 212) to find the slope.

    $m = \dfrac{212 - 32}{100 - 0} = \dfrac{180}{100} = \dfrac{9}{5}$

    The slope is $\dfrac{9}{5}$.

    Use the slope and (0, 32) to find $b$.
    $y = mx + b$

    $32 = \dfrac{9}{5}(0) + b$

    $32 = 0 + b$
    $32 = b$
    The $y$-intercept is 32.
    Substitute into $y = mx + b$.

    $y = \dfrac{9}{5}x + 32.$

11. If $x$ represents the number of hours and $y$ represents the total cost of renting the sailboat, then the equation is $y = 20x + 12$.

12. Since the $y$-intercept is 1,000, the initial deposit was $1,000.

13. Use (0, 1,000) and (2, 2,000) to find the slope.

    $m = \dfrac{2{,}000 - 1{,}000}{2 - 0} = \dfrac{1{,}000}{2} = 500$

    $m = 500$
    Read the $y$-intercept from the graph.
    $b = 1{,}000$

14. $y = 500x + 1{,}000$

15. The amount of money in the savings account increases by $500 each month.

## Focus on Higher Order Thinking

16. Examine the problem and decide what quantity you start with, or the input, and what quantity you are trying to find, or the output. Use the input quantity for $x$ and the output quantity for $y$.

17. The rate of change would not be constant. Using different pairs of points in the slope formula would give you different results.

18. No; A negative value of $m$ means the dependent variable ($y$) is decreasing as the independent variable ($x$) is increasing, so the graph falls from left to right.

## LESSON 5.2

### Your Turn

1.

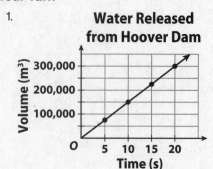

**Water Released from Hoover Dam**

Use (0, 0) and (10, 150,000) to find the slope.

$m = \dfrac{150{,}000 - 0}{10 - 0} = \dfrac{150{,}000}{10} = 15{,}000$

$m = 15{,}000$
Read the $y$-intercept from the graph.
$b = 0$
Substitute into $y = mx + b$
$y = 15{,}000x$

4. Use (4, 550) and (6, 700) to find the slope.

   $m = \dfrac{700 - 550}{6 - 4} = \dfrac{150}{2} = 75$

   Use the slope and (4, 550) to find $b$.
   $y = mx + b$
   $550 = 75(4) + b$
   $550 = 300 + b$
   $250 = b$
   Substitute into $y = mx + b$.
   The equation is $p = 75n + 250$.

5. Use (10, 45) and (20, 50) to find the slope.

   $m = \dfrac{50 - 45}{20 - 10} = \dfrac{5}{10} = 0.50$

Use the slope and $(10, 45)$ to find $b$.
$$y = mx + b$$
$$45 = 0.50(10) + b$$
$$45 = 5 + b$$
$$40 = b$$
Substitute into $y = mx + b$.
The equation is $c = 0.50d + 40$.

## Guided Practice

1.

**Bus Pass Balance**

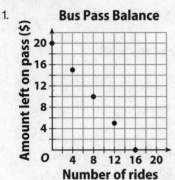

Use $(0, 20)$ and $(8, 10)$ to find the slope.
$$m = \frac{10 - 20}{8 - 0} = \frac{-10}{8} = -\frac{5}{4} = -1.25$$
$$m = -1.25$$
Read the $y$-intercept from the graph.
$b = 20$
Substitute into $y = mx + b$.
$y = -1.25x + 20$

2. Use $(0, 59)$ and $(2{,}000, 51)$ to find the slope.
$$m = \frac{51 - 59}{2{,}000 - 0} = \frac{-8}{2{,}000} = -0.004$$
The slope is $-0.004$.

3. Since, when $x = 0$, the value of $y$ is 59, the $y$-intercept is 59.

4. $y = -0.004x + 59$

5. Find the value of $y$ when $x = 5{,}000$.
$$y = -0.004x + 59$$
$$y = -0.004(5{,}000) + 59$$
$$y = 39$$
At 5,000 feet, the temperature is 39°F.

6. Use two data points from the table to find the slope, and then locate the point on the table where $x$ is 0 to identify the $y$-intercept.

## Independent Practice

7.

**Cost of Large Pizza**

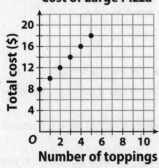

Use $(0, 8)$ and $(1, 10)$ to find the slope.
$$m = \frac{10 - 8}{1 - 0} = \frac{2}{1} = 2$$
$$m = 2$$
Read the $y$-intercept from the graph.
$b = 8$
Substitute into $y = mx + b$.
$C = 2t + 8$

8.

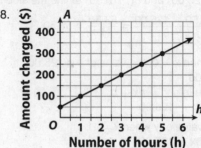

Use $(0, 50)$ and $(1, 100)$ to find the slope.
$$m = \frac{100 - 50}{1 - 0} = \frac{50}{1} = 50$$
$$m = 50$$
Read the $y$-intercept from the graph.
$b = 50$
Substitute into $y = mx + b$.
$A = 50t + 50$

9. a. Use $(0, 30)$ and $(8, 18)$ to find the slope.
$$m = \frac{18 - 30}{8 - 0} = \frac{-12}{8} = -1.50$$
$$m = -1.50$$
Since, when $x = 0$, the value of $y$ is 30, $b = 30$.
Substitute into $y = mx + b$.
$y = -1.50x + 30$

   b. The amount left on the card decreases as the number of car washes increases.

   c. Find the value of $x$ when $y = 0$.
$$y = -1.50x + 30$$
$$0 = -1.50x + 30$$
$$-30 = -1.50x$$
$$20 = x$$
20; after 20 washes, there is no money left on the card.

10. Use $(-2, -1)$ and $(-1, 0)$ to find the slope.
$$m = \frac{0 - (-1)}{-1 - (-2)} = \frac{1}{1} = 1$$
$$m = 1$$
Since, when $x = 0$, the value of $y$ is 1, $b = 1$.
Substitute into $y = mx + b$.
$y = x + 1$

11. Use $(-4, 14)$ and $(1, 4)$ to find the slope.
$$m = \frac{4 - 14}{1 - (-4)} = \frac{-10}{5} = -2$$
$$m = -2$$
Since, when $x = 0$, the value of $y$ is 6, $b = 6$.
Substitute into $y = mx + b$.
$y = -2x + 6$

**12. a.**

| Month, $x$ | 0 | 1 | 2 | 3 | 4 |
|---|---|---|---|---|---|
| Amount in savings (\$), $y$ | 125.00 | 178.50 | 232.00 | 285.50 | 339.00 |

b. Use $(0, 125.00)$ and $(1, 178.50)$ to find the slope.

$$m = \frac{178.50 - 125.00}{1 - 0} = \frac{53.50}{1} = 53.50$$

$m = 53.50$

Since, when $x = 0$, the value of $y$ is 125.00, $b = 125.00$.

Substitute into $y = mx + b$.

$y = 53.50x + 125.00$

c. Find the value of $y$ when $x = 11$.

$y = 53.50x + 125.00$

$y = 53.50(11) + 125.00$

$y = 713.50$

After 11 months, Desiree will have \$713.50.

**13. a.** No; The rate of change between pairs of values is not constant.

b. No; There is no apparent pattern in the values in the table.

### Focus on Higher Order Thinking

14. If there is an $x$-value of 0 in the table, then the $y$-value for that $x$-value is $b$, since the $x$-value of the $y$-intercept is 0.

15. 0; Jamie's graph contained $(0, 0)$. Since Jayla's data were the same, but with $x$ and $y$ switched, her graph also contained $(0, 0)$.

## LESSON 5.3

### Your Turn

1. Use $(5, 40)$ and $(10, 60)$ to find the slope.

$$m = \frac{60 - 40}{10 - 5} = \frac{20}{5} = 4$$

Use the slope and $(5, 40)$ to find $b$.

$y = mx + b$

$40 = 4(5) + b$

$40 = 20 + b$

$20 = b$

Substitute into $y = mx + b$.

The equation is $y = 4x + 20$.

2. Use $(2, 480)$ and $(15, 3,600)$ to find the slope.

$$m = \frac{3,600 - 480}{15 - 2} = \frac{3,120}{13} = 240$$

Use the slope and $(2, 480)$ to find $b$.

$y = mx + b$

$480 = 240(2) + b$

$480 = 480 + b$

$0 = b$

Substitute into $y = mx + b$.

The equation is $y = 240x$.

6. The graph contains the point $(2, 30)$, so she earned \$30 for working 2 hours.

7. Use $(0, 0)$ and $(2, 30)$ to find the slope.

$$m = \frac{30 - 0}{2 - 0} = \frac{30}{2} = 15$$

Since the graph contains $(0, 0)$, $b = 0$, and the equation is $y = 15x$.

Find the value of $y$ when $x = 3.25$.

$y = 15x$

$y = 15(3.25)$

$y = 48.75$

She earned \$48.75 for working 3.25 hours.

8. $5 \times 8 = 40$

Find the value of $y$ when $x = 40$.

$y = 15x$

$y = 15(40)$

$y = 600$

She earned \$600 for working five 8-hour days.

### Guided Practice

1. Use $(2, 60)$ and $(4, 120)$ to find the slope.

$$m = \frac{120 - 60}{4 - 2} = \frac{60}{2} = 30$$

Use the slope and $(2, 60)$ to find $b$.

$y = mx + b$

$60 = 30(2) + b$

$60 = 60 + b$

$0 = b$

Substitute into $y = mx + b$.

The equation is $y = 30x$.

2. Use $(4, 12)$ and $(8, 22)$ to find the slope.

$$m = \frac{22 - 12}{8 - 4} = \frac{10}{4} = 2.5$$

Use the slope and $(4, 12)$ to find $b$.

$y = mx + b$

$12 = 2.5(4) + b$

$12 = 10 + b$

$2 = b$

Substitute into $y = mx + b$.

The equation is $y = 2.5x + 2$.

3. Use $(1, 50)$ and $(2, 70)$ to find the slope.

$$m = \frac{70 - 50}{2 - 1} = \frac{20}{1} = 20$$

Use the slope and $(1, 50)$ to find $b$.

$y = mx + b$

$50 = 20(1) + b$

$50 = 20 + b$

$30 = b$

Substitute into $y = mx + b$.

The equation is $y = 20x + 30$.

Find the value of $y$ when $x = 5.5$.

$y = 20x + 30$

$y = 20(5.5) + 30$

$y = 140$

The cost of a rental that lasts 5.5 hours is \$140.

4. Yes; because the graph has a constant rate of change.

5. No; because the graph does not have a constant rate of change.

6. Sample answer: Graph the data points. If the points lie along a straight line, the data is linear.

## Independent Practice

7. Find the rate of change.

$$\frac{45 - 15}{9 - 3} = \frac{30}{6} = 5$$

$$\frac{105 - 45}{21 - 9} = \frac{60}{12} = 5$$

Yes; because the rate of change is constant.

8. Find the rate of change.

$$\frac{76.8 - 30}{8 - 5} = \frac{46.8}{3} = 15.6$$

$$\frac{235.2 - 76.8}{14 - 8} = \frac{158.4}{6} = 26.4$$

No; because the rate of change is not constant.

9. The relationship is linear because the rate of change is the cost of a DVD, which is constant.

10. The relationship is not linear because the rate of growth decreases as a person gets older.

11. The relationship is not linear because the rate of change in the area of a square increases as the side length increases.

12. The relationship is linear because the rate of change between the two units is the conversion factor, which is constant.

13.

**Mars Rover**

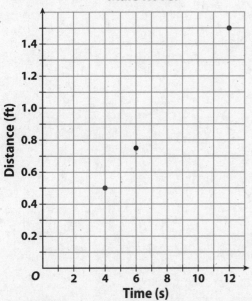

The three points lie along a straight line. Therefore, the relationship is linear.
Use (4, 0.5) and (6, 0.75) to find the slope.

$$m = \frac{0.75 - 0.5}{6 - 4} = \frac{0.25}{2} = 0.125$$

Use the slope and (4, 0.5) to find $b$.

$$y = mx + b$$
$$0.5 = 0.125(4) + b$$
$$0.5 = 0.5 + b$$
$$0 = b$$

Substitute into $y = mx + b$.
The equation is $y = 0.125x$.

Since 1 minute = 60 seconds, find the value of $y$ when $x = 60$.

$$y = 0.125x$$
$$y = 0.125(60)$$
$$y = 7.5$$

In 1 minute, the Mars Rover would travel 7.5 feet.

14. Yes; Decreasing the value of $b$ by 4 decreases the value of $mx + b$ by 4 because the value of $mx$ stays the same.

## Focus on Higher Order Thinking

15. Sample answer: Because an $x$-value of 6 lies halfway between the $x$-values of 4 and 8, the corresponding $y$-value will lie halfway between the $y$-values of 38 and 76.

16. No; The rate of change must be constant, and the rate of change is the difference in $y$-values divided by the difference in the corresponding $x$-values.

17. Sample answer: Find the equation of the linear relationship using the slope and the given point. Then substitute any $x$-value to find the corresponding $y$-value.

18. He calculated the slope incorrectly. He should have written $m = \frac{18.45 - 17.5}{18 - 7}$.

## MODULE 5

### Ready to Go On?

1. Use (0, 20) and (2, 80) to find the slope.

$$m = \frac{80 - 20}{2 - 0} = \frac{60}{2} = 30$$

Read the $y$-intercept from the graph.
$b = 20$
Substitute into $y = mx + b$.
The equation is $y = 30x + 20$.

2. Use (0, 60) and (6, 0) to find the slope.

$$m = \frac{0 - 60}{6 - 0} = \frac{-60}{6} = -10$$

Read the $y$-intercept from the graph.
$b = 60$
Substitute into $y = mx + b$.
The equation is $y = -10x + 60$.

3. Use (0, 1.5) and (100, 36.5) to find the slope.

$$m = \frac{36.5 - 1.5}{100 - 0} = \frac{35}{100} = 0.35$$

Since, when $x = 0$, the value of $y$ is 1.5, $b = 1.5$.
Substitute into $y = mx + b$.
The equation is $y = 0.35x + 1.5$.

4. Use (25, 94) and (35, 88) to find the slope.

$$m = \frac{88 - 94}{35 - 25} = \frac{-6}{10} = -0.6$$

Use the slope and (25, 94) to find $b$.

$$y = mx + b$$
$$94 = -0.6(25) + b$$
$$94 = -15 + b$$
$$109 = b$$

Substitute into $y = mx + b$.
The equation is $y = -0.6x + 109$.

5. Use (20, 40) and (50, 60) to find the slope.

$m = \dfrac{60 - 40}{50 - 20} = \dfrac{20}{30} = \dfrac{2}{3}$

Use the slope and (20, 40) to find $b$.

$y = mx + b$

$40 = \dfrac{2}{3}(20) + b$

$40 = \dfrac{40}{3} + b$

$\dfrac{80}{3} = b$

Substitute into $y = mx + b$.

The equation is $y = \dfrac{2}{3}x + \dfrac{80}{3}$.

6. Use (30, 50) and (40, 20) to find the slope.

$m = \dfrac{20 - 50}{40 - 30} = \dfrac{-30}{10} = -3$

Use the slope and (30, 50) to find $b$.

$y = mx + b$

$50 = -3(30) + b$

$50 = -90 + b$

$140 = b$

Substitute into $y = mx + b$.

The equation is $y = -3x + 140$.

7. Sample answer: A video game rental store charges $3 per game and a membership fee of $10.

## Are You Ready?

1. $2x + 3$ for $x = 3$
   $2(3) + 3$
   $6 + 3$
   $9$

2. $-4x + 7$ for $x = -1$
   $-4(-1) + 7$
   $4 + 7$
   $11$

3. $1.5x - 2.5$ for $x = 3$
   $1.5(3) - 2.5$
   $4.5 - 2.5$
   $2$

4. $0.4x + 6.1$ for $x = -5$
   $0.4(-5) + 6.1$
   $-2 + 6.1$
   $4.1$

5. $\frac{2}{3}x - 12$ for $x = 18$

   $\frac{2}{3}(18) - 12$

   $\frac{2}{1\cancel{3}}(\cancel{18}^{6}) - 12$

   $12 - 12$
   $0$

6. $-\frac{5}{8}x + 10$ for $x = -8$

   $-\frac{5}{8}(-8) + 10$

   $-\frac{5}{1\cancel{8}}(\cancel{-8}^{-1}) + 10$

   $5 + 10$
   $15$

7. $j =$ Jana's age; $s =$ sister's age; $j + 5 = s$

8. $a =$ Andrew's class; $l =$ Lauren's class; $a = 3 + l$

9. $b =$ bank's height; $f =$ firehouse's height; $b = f - 50$

10. $p =$ pencils; $\frac{p}{6} = 2$

## LESSON 6.1

### Your Turn

4. The relationship is a function; Each input value is paired with only one output value.

5. The relationship is not a function; The input value is paired with more than one output value.

7. The relationship is a function; Each input value is paired with only one output value.

8. The relationship is not a function; The input value 8 is paired with more than one output value.

10. The relationship is not a function; Two input values, 70 and 71, are paired with more than one output value: (70, 164) and (70, 174).

## Guided Practice

1. Each output value is 20 times the corresponding input value.

| Input | Output |
|---|---|
| Tickets | Cost ($) |
| 2 | 40 |
| 5 | 100 |
| 7 | 140 |
| x | 20x |
| 10 | 200 |

2. Each output value is half the corresponding input value.

| Input | Output |
|---|---|
| Minutes | Pages |
| 2 | 1 |
| 10 | 5 |
| 20 | 10 |
| x | $\frac{x}{2}$ |
| 30 | 15 |

3. Each output value is 2.25 times the corresponding input value.

| Input | Output |
|---|---|
| Muffins | Cost ($) |
| 1 | 2.25 |
| 3 | 6.75 |
| 6 | 13.50 |
| x | 2.25x |
| 12 | 27.00 |

4. The relationship is a function; Each input value is paired with only one output value.

5. The relationship is not a function; The input value 4 is paired with more than one output value.

6. Yes; Each input value is paired with only one output value.

7. Mapping diagrams, tables, graphs, ordered pairs; A relationship is a function if each input value is paired with only one output value.

### Independent Practice

8. The relationship is a function; Each input value is paired with only one output value.

9. The relationship is not a function; The input value 5 is paired with more than one output value.

10. Yes; For each pound of aluminum he recycles (input), there can only be one dollar amount representing the amount of money he receives (output).

11. a. For each number of hours there is only one count of the number of bacteria, so each input is paired with only one output.

b. Yes; Each input value would still be paired with only one output value.

12. Check students' work.

13. Yes; Each input value (the weight) is paired with only one output value (the price).

14. No; For any given weight, there will be only one corresponding price.

### Focus on Higher Order Thinking

15. It does not represent a function. For the three input values to be paired with all four output values, at least one of the input values would be paired with more than one output value.

16. The number of days it will take to harvest the onions depends on the number of workers he hires. The input values of the function are the number of workers. The output values are the number of days. For any particular number of workers, the job will take a certain number of days.

## LESSON 6.2

### Your Turn

2. Since the equation is of the form $y = mx + b$ with $b = 0$, the relationship is proportional.

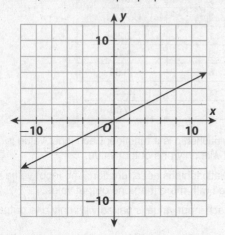

3. Substitute the given values from the table into the equation $y = \frac{2}{3}x$ to find the missing values.

$y = \frac{2}{3}x$         $y = \frac{2}{3}x$

$y = \frac{2}{3}(0)$        $y = \frac{2}{3}(3)$

$y = 0$           $y = 2$

$y = \frac{2}{3}x$         $y = \frac{2}{3}x$

$4 = \frac{2}{3}x$         $y = \frac{2}{3}(9)$

$4 \cdot \frac{3}{2} = x$      $y = 6$

$6 = x$

| Time (min), x | 0 | 3 | 6 | 9 |
|---|---|---|---|---|
| Amount (gal), y | 0 | 2 | 4 | 6 |

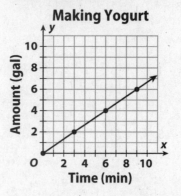

**Making Yogurt**

Since the points lie along a straight line, the relationship is linear. Since the graph contains the origin, the relationship is proportional.

### Guided Practice

1. Substitute the given values from the table into the equation $y = 5 - 2x$ to find the missing values.

$y = 5 - 2x$          $y = 5 - 2x$

$y = 5 - 2(-1)$        $y = 5 - 2(1)$

$y = 7$            $y = 3$

$y = 5 - 2x$          $y = 5 - 2x$

$y = 5 - 2(3)$         $y = 5 - 2(5)$

$y = -1$           $y = -5$

| Input, x | −1 | 1 | 3 | 5 |
|---|---|---|---|---|
| Output, y | 7 | 3 | −1 | −5 |

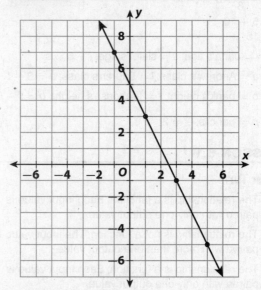

Since the points lie along a straight line, the function is linear.

2. Substitute the given values from the table into the equation $y = 2 - x^2$ to find the missing values.

$y = 2 - x^2$
$y = 2 - (-2)^2$
$y = 2 - 4$
$y = -2$

$y = 2 - x^2$
$y = 2 - (-1)^2$
$y = 2 - 1$
$y = 1$

$y = 2 - x^2$
$y = 2 - (0)^2$
$y = 2 - 0$
$y = 2$

$y = 2 - x^2$
$y = 2 - (1)^2$
$y = 2 - 1$
$y = 1$

$y = 2 - 2^2$
$y = 2 - (2)^2$
$y = 2 - 4$
$y = -2$

| Input, x | −2 | −1 | 0 | 1 | 2 |
|----------|----|----|---|---|---|
| Output, y | −2 | 1 | 2 | 1 | −2 |

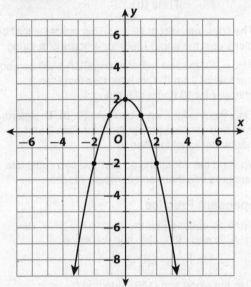

Since the points do not lie along a straight line, the function is nonlinear.

3. The equation is not linear because it cannot be written in the form $y = mx + b$.

4. Since the equation can be written as $y = -x + 1$, which is in the form $y = mx + b$, the equation is linear.

5. A table of values will include (0, 0) and show a constant rate of change. An equation will be of the form $y = mx$. A graph will be a line passing through the origin.

## Independent Practice

6. Since the equation is of the form $y = mx + b$ with $b \neq 0$, the relationship is nonproportional.

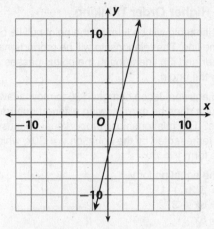

7. The relationship is neither linear nor proportional because the variable, $x$, is squared. The equation cannot be written in the form $y = mx$.

8. Since the equation can be written as $y = -x + 20$, which is in the form $y = mx + b$, the equation is linear. Since $b \neq 0$, it is not proportional.

9. a.

**Drill Team Uniforms**

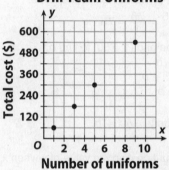

Yes; Since the points lie along a straight line, the function is linear.

b. Since the $y$-values increase by 60 as the $x$-values increase by 1, the $y$-value corresponding to an $x$-value of 12 would be 720. Therefore, 12 uniforms cost $720.

10. Yes; Since the points lie along a straight line, the relationship is linear. Since the graph contains the origin, the relationship is proportional.

11. Disagree; The equation can be written in the form $y = mx + b$, with $m = 0$. The graph of the equation is a horizontal line.

12. The equation is $y = 30x + 70$; Find the value of $y$ when $x = 3$.
$y = 30x + 70$
$y = 30(3) + 70$
$y = 90 + 70$
$y = 160$

You will have read 160 pages.

## Focus on Higher Order Thinking

13. The relationship will be linear if the points all lie on the same line. The relationship will be proportional if it is linear and if a line through the points passes through the origin.

14. Sample answer: Jacob charges $30 to mow a lawn. How much does he earn mowing different numbers of lawns? The relationship is proportional because it can be represented by the equation $y = 30x$, which is in the form $y = mx$.

15. Solve the equation for $y$.

$$y + 3 = 3(2x + 1)$$
$$y + 3 = 6x + 3$$
$$y = 6x$$

The equation is in the form $y = mx + b$, so it is linear. Since $b = 0$, it represents a proportional relationship.

# LESSON 6.3

## Your Turn

1. Write an equation for the data in the table. Use (1, 7.50) and (2, 15.00) to find the slope.

$$m = \frac{15 - 7.5}{2 - 1} = \frac{7.5}{1} = 7.5$$

Use the slope and (1, 7.50) to find $b$.
$$y = mx + b$$
$$7.50 = 7.5(1) + b$$
$$7.50 = 7.5 + b$$
$$0 = b$$

Substitute into $y = mx + b$.

$$y = 7.5x$$

For each equation, find the value of $y$ when $x = 6$.

$y = 6.95x + 1.50$     $y = 7.5x$
$y = 6.95(6) + 1.50$     $y = 7.5(6)$
$y = 43.20$     $y = 45$

For 6 books, buying the books at the bookstore is more expensive ($45 vs. $43.20).

## Guided Practice

1. Write an equation for the data in the table. Use (20, 194) and (30, 187) to find the slope.

$$m = \frac{187 - 194}{30 - 20} = \frac{-7}{10} = -0.7$$

Use the slope and (20, 194) to find $b$.

$$y = mx + b$$
$$194 = -0.7(20) + b$$
$$194 = -14 + b$$
$$208 = b$$

Substitute into $y = mx + b$.

$$y = -0.7x + 208$$

For each equation, find the value of $y$ when $x = 70$.

$y = 220 - x$     $y = -0.7x + 208$
$y = 220 - 70$     $y = -0.7(70) + 208$
$y = 150$     $y = 159$

For a 70-year old, the second method gives the greater maximum heart rate (159 bpm vs. 150 bpm).

2. Check to see if $y = 0$ when $x = 0$.

$y = 220 - x$     $y = -0.7x + 208$
$y = 220 - 0$     $y = -0.7(0) + 208$
$y = 220$     $y = 208$

For both methods, the relationship between heart rate and age is nonproportional.

3. The $y$-intercept is 40 and the slope is $\frac{5}{1}$.

Students pay a $40 fee and $5 per hour.

4.
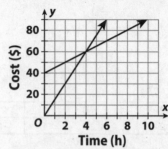

5. The lines intersect at (4, 60). This indicates that both plans cost the same ($60) for 4 hours of tutoring.

6. At $x = 10$, the line representing Plan 1 will be above the line for Plan 2. This indicates that Plan 2 is cheaper for 10 hours of tutoring.

7. Only the line for Plan 1 contains (0, 0). Therefore, cost and time are proportional for Plan 1 and nonproportional for Plan 2.

8. You find the equations so that you can substitute numbers into them and compare results.

## Independent Practice

9. Write an equation for the data in the table. Use (150, 2) and (300, 4) to find the slope.

$$m = \frac{4 - 2}{300 - 150} = \frac{2}{150} = \frac{1}{75}$$

Use the slope and (150, 2) to find $b$.
$$y = mx + b$$
$$2 = \frac{1}{75}(150) + b$$
$$2 = 2 + b$$
$$0 = b$$
Substitute into $y = mx + b$.

$$y = \frac{1}{75}x$$

Write an equation for the line representing Scooter B.
The $y$-intercept is 0 and the slope is $\frac{1}{90}$.

Substitute into $y = mx + b$.

$$y = \frac{1}{90}x$$

For each equation, find the value of $y$ when $x = 1350$.

$y = \frac{1}{75}x$        $y = \frac{1}{90}x$

$y = \frac{1}{75}(1,350)$    $y = \frac{1}{90}(1,350)$

$y = 18$        $y = 15$

When 1,350 miles are driven, Scooter B uses fewer gallons of gas (15 gal vs. 18 gal).

10. Since both equations are in the form $y = mx$, the amount of gas used and the number of miles driven are proportional for both scooters.

11. Write an equation for the data in the table. Use (100, 20) and (200, 25) to find the slope.

$$m = \frac{25 - 20}{200 - 100} = \frac{5}{100} = \frac{1}{20}$$

Use the slope and (100, 20) to find $b$.

$y = mx + b$

$20 = \frac{1}{20}(100) + b$

$20 = 5 + b$

$15 = b$

Substitute into $y = mx + b$.

$y = \frac{1}{20}x + 15$

For each equation, find the value of $y$ when $x = 199$.

$y = 0.10x + 5$      $y = \frac{1}{20}x + 15$

$y = 0.10(199) + 5$      $y = \frac{1}{20}(199) + 15$

$y = 24.90$      $y = 24.95$

For fewer than 200 texts, the first plan is cheaper ($24.90 vs. $24.95).

12. This indicates that the relationship between the number of texts and the cost is nonproportional. There is a monthly charge of $5 even if no texting occurs.

13. The equation representing the plan at the first store is $y = 20x + 50$.
For each equation, find the value of $y$ when $x = 12$.

$y = 20x + 50$      $y = 15x + 80$

$y = 20(12) + 50$      $y = 15(12) + 80$

$y = 290$      $y = 260$

When paid off in 12 months, the camera at the second store is cheaper ($260 vs. $290).

14. The unit rate for the data in the table is $\frac{10}{2}$, or 5, so the French club earns $5 per car.

The slope of the graph is $\frac{8}{1}$, so the soccer team earns $8 per car.

The soccer team makes the most money per car. The unit rate for their earnings is $8 per car. The unit rate for the French club's earnings is $5 per car.

## Focus on Higher Order Thinking

15. Since the rate per visit is the same ($5), and the monthly fee at Gym A is greater than the monthly fee at Gym B ($60 vs. $40), the cost at Gym A will always be greater than the cost at Gym B.

16. The value of the two functions is the same when $x = 1$, but as $x$ increases, the function $y = 5x + 1$ will increase more quickly because the slope is greater. A graph of the two lines would show that the line representing $y = 5x + 1$ is steeper than the line representing $y = 4x + 2$.

17. $y = -24x + 8$; The graph of $y = -24x + 8$ is steeper than the graph of $y = -21x + 9$ because the absolute value of $-24$ is greater than the absolute value of $-21$.

## LESSON 6.4

### Guided Practice

1. The graph has a steep positive slope; Sample answer: The graph is increasing quickly. This shows a period of rapid growth.

2. The graph has a negative slope; Sample answer: The number of bacteria is decreasing.

3. Graph 2 starts with a positive slope, meaning Chip's speed is increasing. It then switches to a negative slope, meaning Chip's speed is decreasing. Next it shows a speed of 0 and stays that way for a short period of time, with a slope of 0, meaning that Chip has stopped. Finally, it again shows a positive slope, meaning Chip's speed is increasing. Graph 2 corresponds to the situation.

4. Graph 3 starts with a positive slope, meaning Linda's speed is increasing. It then switches to a negative slope, meaning Linda's speed is decreasing. Graph 3 corresponds to the situation.

5. The graph should start with a slope of 0, representing Paulo walking to the end of the board. It should then have a negative slope, representing Paulo diving forward into the water. Next, it should switch back to a slope of 0, representing Paulo swimming straight forward while underwater. Finally, it should have a positive slope, representing Paulo swimming forward and upward to the surface of the water.

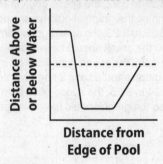

**Distance from Edge of Pool**

### Independent Practice

6. Graph 3 starts with a positive slope, meaning that Arnold's distance from home is increasing. It then switches to a slope of 0, meaning that Arnold's distance from home is neither increasing nor decreasing. In other words, he is staying in one spot. Finally, it again shows a positive slope, meaning that Arnold's distance from home is increasing. Graph 3 corresponds to the situation.

7. Graph 1 starts with a positive slope, meaning that Francisco's distance from home is increasing. It then switches to a slope of 0, meaning that Francisco's distance from home is neither increasing nor decreasing. In other words, he is staying in one spot. Finally, it shows a negative slope, meaning that Francisco's distance from home is decreasing. Graph 1 corresponds to the situation.

8. Graph 2 shows a positive slope, meaning that Celia's distance from home is increasing. Graph 2 corresponds to the situation.

9. The graph first shows a positive slope, meaning that Regina's distance from the rental site is initially increasing. It then switches to a slope of 0, meaning that she stops for a short period of time. Next it briefly shows a negative slope, meaning that her distance from the rental site is decreasing. It then switches back to a positive slope, meaning that her distance from the rental site is increasing. After that it shows a slope of 0, meaning that she again stops briefly. Finally, it switches to a negative slope, meaning her distance from the rental site is decreasing; Sample answer: Regina left the rental shop and rode for an hour. She took a half-hour rest and then started back. She changed her mind and continued for another half hour. She took a half-hour break and then returned to the rental shop.

10. Regina covered the greatest distance during the half-hour interval for which the slope of the graph is the steepest. Regina covered the greatest distance from 0.5 to 1.0 hour.

11. From 3:20 to 3:21, the speed goes from 0 mi/hr to 14 mi/hr, so the graph should have a positive slope. From 3:21 to 3:22, the speed goes from 14 mi/hr to 41 mi/hr, so the graph should have a positive slope. From 3:22 to 3:23, the speed goes from 41 mph to 62 mph, so the graph should have a positive slope. From 3:23 to 3:24, the speed goes from 62 mi/hr to 8 mi/hr, so the graph should have a negative slope. Finally, from 3:24 to 3:25, the speed goes from 8 mi/hr to 0 mi/hr, so the graph should have a negative slope.

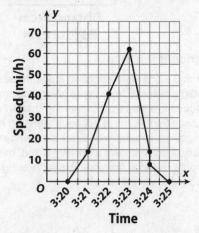

12. The ride's speed is increasing the fastest when the slope of the graph is steepest when positive. The ride's speed is increasing the fastest from 3:21 to 3:22.

13. The ride's speed is decreasing the fastest when the slope of the graph is steepest when negative. The ride's speed is decreasing the fastest from 3:23 to 3:24.

## Focus on Higher Order Thinking

14. Before time $t$, the slope of the graph is initially negative but then turns positive; Sample answer: The population is decreasing at first, but begins to increase again. The graph declines but then begins to rise midway through the time period.

15. The general shape of the graph after time $t$ might remain the same, but the portion of the graph after time $t$ would be shifted upwards, since a large group of foxes has been moved to the island.

**Fox Population**

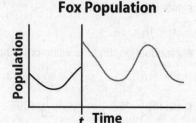

16. When the forest fire destroys part of the woodland area on the island, the fox population would suddenly decrease sharply. Then the situation would slowly return to normal; Sample answer: The graph would show a steep decline at the point that represents the fire. Then as the forest re-grows, the gradual increasing and decreasing pattern would resume.

## MODULE 6

### Ready to Go On?

1. The relationship is not a function. The input value 5 is paired with more than one output value.

2. The relationship is a function. Each input value is paired with only one output value.

3. The relationship is not a function. The input value 2 is paired with more than one output value.

4. Since the equation representing the situation can be written as $y = 14x$, which is in the form $y = mx$, the situation is both linear and proportional.

5. Since the equation representing the situation can be written as $y = 50x + 5$, which is in the form $y = mx + b$, the situation is linear. Since $b \neq 0$, the situation is nonproportional.

6. The slope of the line representing function 1 is $\frac{-4}{1}$, or $-4$. The rate of change of the data in the table is $\frac{6.5 - 11}{3 - 2} = -4.5$. Since the absolute value of $-4.5$ is greater than the absolute value of $-4$, function 2 is changing more quickly.

7. It can be described as a line that starts at (0,0) with a constant positive slope.

8. You can use functions written as tables, graphs, or equations to find an unknown value, or to predict a value.

# Solutions Key
## Solving Equations and Systems of Equations

**MODULE 7** *Equations and Inequalities with the Variable on Both Sides*

### Are You Ready?

1. 8: 8, 16, 24
   12: 12, 24
   LCD(8, 12) = 24

2. 9: 9, 18, 27, 36
   12: 12, 24, 36
   LCD(9, 12) = 36

3. 15: 15, 30, 45, 60
   20: 20, 40, 60
   LCD(15, 20) = 60

4. 8: 8, 16, 24, 32, 40
   10: 10, 20, 30, 40
   LCD(8, 10) = 40

5. $0.683 \times 100 = 68.3$

6. $9.15 \times 1,000 = 9,150$

7. $0.005 \times 10 = 0.05$

8. $1,000 \times 1,000 = 1,000,000$

9. The difference between three times a number and 7 is 14: $3x - 7 = 14$

10. The quotient of five times a number and 7 is no more than 10: $\frac{5x}{7} \leq 10$

11. 14 less than 3 times a number is 5 more than half of the number: $3x - 14 = \frac{1}{2}x + 5$

### LESSON 7.1

**Your Turn**

2. Let $x$ represent the number of weeks.
$$
\begin{aligned}
256 - 3x &= 384 - 5x \\
\underline{+ 5x} &\quad \underline{+ 5x} \\
256 + 2x &= 384 \\
\underline{-256} &\quad \underline{-256} \\
2x &= 128 \\
\frac{2x}{2} &= \frac{128}{2} \\
x &= 64
\end{aligned}
$$
The amount of water will be the same after 64 weeks.

3. Sample answer: One tennis club charges $30 per session to play tennis. Another tennis club charges an annual fee of $48 plus $22 per session. After how many sessions is the cost at the two clubs the same?

### Guided Practice

1.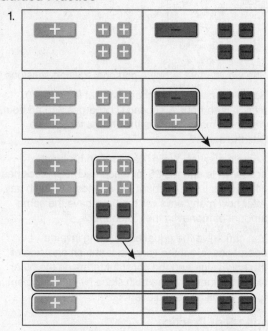

$x = -4$

2.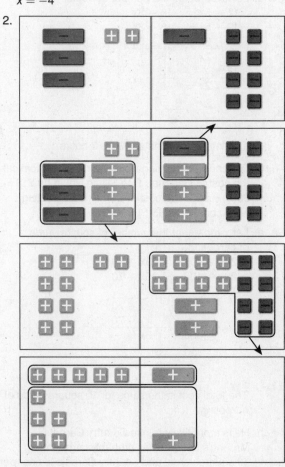

$x = 5$

3. Let $x$ represent the number of training sessions.

$$25 + 30x = 65 + 20x$$
$$\underline{\quad - 20x \qquad - 20x \quad}$$
$$25 + 10x = 65$$
$$\underline{-25 \qquad\quad -25 \quad}$$
$$10x = 40$$
$$\frac{10x}{10} = \frac{40}{10}$$
$$x = 4$$

She would have to buy 4 personal training sessions.

4. Sample answer: A DJ charges a flat fee of $120 plus $25 an hour. A second DJ charges $45 an hour. After how many hours is the charge for the two DJs the same?

5. Sample answer: Xavier has $100 in his lunch account. He spends $6 for lunch each day. Zack has $160 in his lunch account. He spends $10 each day. After how many days will the boys have the same amount of money in their accounts?

6. You can solve the equation by using inverse operations to get the variable terms on one side of the equal sign and the constant terms on the other side, and then dividing both sides by the coefficient of the resulting variable term.

## Independent Practice

7. a. Let $x$ represent the number of hours.

$$12 + 5x = 18 + 3x$$
$$12 + 5x = 18 + 3x$$
$$\underline{\quad - 3x \qquad - 3x \quad}$$
$$12 + 2x = 18$$
$$\underline{-12 \qquad\quad -12 \quad}$$
$$2x = 6$$
$$\frac{2x}{2} = \frac{6}{2}$$
$$x = 3$$

The total cost is the same for 3 hours.

b. Darlene's Dog Sitting would be more economical; the cost at Darlene's Dog Sitting would be $18 + $3(5) = $33. The cost at Derrick's Dog Sitting would be $12 + $5(5) = $37.

8. a. Let $x$ represent the number of square yards of carpeting.

$$22x + 100 = 25x + 70$$
$$22x + 100 = 25x + 70$$
$$\underline{-22x \qquad\quad -22x \quad}$$
$$100 = 3x + 70$$
$$\underline{-70 \qquad\quad - 70 \quad}$$
$$30 = 3x$$
$$\frac{30}{3} = \frac{3x}{3}$$
$$10 = x$$

The total cost is the same for 10 square yards of carpeting.

b. He is more likely to hire Country Carpets; Mr. Shu's basement is probably larger than 10 square yards, and Country Carpets is cheaper than City Carpets for areas greater than 10 square yards.

9. Let $x$ represent the number.

$$3x - 2 = x + 10$$
$$3x - 2 = x + 10$$
$$\underline{-x \qquad\quad -x \quad}$$
$$2x - 2 = 10$$
$$\underline{+ 2 \qquad\quad + 2 \quad}$$
$$2x = 12$$
$$\frac{2x}{2} = \frac{12}{2}$$
$$x = 6$$

10. Let $x$ represent the number.

$$x + 4 = 19 - 2x$$
$$x + 4 = 19 - 2x$$
$$\underline{+ 2x \qquad\quad + 2x \quad}$$
$$3x + 4 = 19$$
$$\underline{-4 \qquad\quad -4 \quad}$$
$$3x = 15$$
$$\frac{3x}{3} = \frac{15}{3}$$
$$x = 5$$

11. Let $x$ represent the number.

$$8x - 20 = x + 15$$
$$8x - 20 = x + 15$$
$$\underline{-x \qquad\quad -x \quad}$$
$$7x - 20 = 15$$
$$\underline{+ 20 \qquad +20 \quad}$$
$$7x = 35$$
$$\frac{7x}{7} = \frac{35}{7}$$
$$x = 5$$

12. a. Let $x$ represent the number of minutes.

$$35 + 3x = 45 + 2x$$
$$\underline{\quad - 2x \qquad - 2x \quad}$$
$$35 + x = 45$$
$$\underline{-35 \qquad\quad - 35 \quad}$$
$$x = 10$$

The cost will be the same for a call lasting 10 minutes.

b. Company B is a better choice whenever you expect to make a call that will be over 10 minutes.

## Focus on Higher Order Thinking

13. Let $x$ represent the number of chairs in each row.

$$9x + 3 = 7x + 19$$
$$\underline{-7x \qquad\quad -7x \quad}$$
$$2x + 3 = 19$$
$$\underline{- 3 \qquad\quad -3 \quad}$$
$$2x = 16$$
$$\frac{2x}{2} = \frac{16}{2}$$
$$x = 8$$

There are 8 chairs in each row.
$9(8) + 3 = 7(8) + 19 = 75$
Liam has 75 chairs.

14. Delia multiplied the flat fee, instead of the daily rate, by the number of days $x$. The total cost for each company is the flat fee plus the product of the daily rate and the number of days; $365 + 125x = 250 + 175x$.

15. Let $x$ represent the number of miles in each lap.

$$
\begin{array}{rl}
3x + 6 =& 5x + 2 \\
\underline{-3x} & \underline{-3x} \\
6 =& 2x + 2 \\
\underline{-2} & \underline{-2} \\
4 =& 2x \\
\dfrac{4}{2} =& \dfrac{2x}{2} \\
2 =& x
\end{array}
$$

Each lap is 2 miles.
$3(2) + 6 = 5(2) + 2 = 12$ miles
She runs 12 miles each day, so she runs 6 laps on Saturday.

## LESSON 7.2

### Your Turn

3. Multiply both sides of the equation by 7.

$$
7\left(\dfrac{1}{7}k - 6\right) = 7\left(\dfrac{3}{7}k + 4\right)
$$

$$
\begin{array}{rl}
k - 42 =& 3k + 28 \\
\underline{-k} & \underline{-k} \\
-42 =& 2k + 28 \\
\underline{-28} & \underline{-28} \\
-70 =& 2k \\
\dfrac{-70}{2} =& \dfrac{2k}{2} \\
-35 =& k
\end{array}
$$

4. Multiply both sides of the equation by 12.

$$
12\left(\dfrac{5}{6}y + 1\right) = 12\left(-\dfrac{1}{2}y + \dfrac{1}{4}\right)
$$

$$
\begin{array}{rl}
10y + 12 =& -6y + 3 \\
\underline{+6y} & \underline{+6y} \\
16y + 12 =& 3 \\
\underline{-12} & \underline{-12} \\
16y =& -9 \\
\dfrac{16y}{16} =& \dfrac{-9}{16} \\
y =& -\dfrac{9}{16}
\end{array}
$$

5. Let $x$ represent the weight of 1 cubic foot of water.
   $1.9x = 1.3x + 37.44$
   Multiply both sides of the equation by 100.

$$
\begin{array}{rl}
100(1.9x) =& 100(1.3x + 37.44) \\
190x =& 130x + 3{,}744 \\
\underline{-130x} & \underline{-130x} \\
60x =& 3{,}744 \\
\dfrac{60x}{60} =& \dfrac{3{,}744}{60} \\
x =& 62.4
\end{array}
$$

The weight of 1 cubic foot of water is 62.4 lb.

6. Sample answer: A bin of rice at a store is $\dfrac{1}{3}$ full. After 10 additional pounds of rice is added to the bin, the bin is $\dfrac{3}{5}$ full. How much rice does the bin hold when it is full?

### Guided Practice

1. a. Let $x$ represent the number of months.
   $60 + 50.45x = 57.95x$

   b. Multiply both sides of the equation by 100.

$$
\begin{array}{rl}
100(60 + 50.45x) =& 100(57.95x) \\
6{,}000 + 5{,}045x =& 5{,}795x \\
\underline{-5{,}045x} & \underline{-5{,}045x} \\
6{,}000 =& 750x \\
\dfrac{6{,}000}{750} =& \dfrac{750x}{750} \\
8 =& x
\end{array}
$$

The cost is the same for 8 months of service.

2. Multiply both sides of the equation by 4.

$$
4\left(\dfrac{3}{4}n - 18\right) = 4\left(\dfrac{1}{4}n - 4\right)
$$

$$
\begin{array}{rl}
3n - 72 =& n - 16 \\
\underline{-n} & \underline{-n} \\
2n - 72 =& -16 \\
\underline{+72} & \underline{+72} \\
2n =& 56 \\
\dfrac{2n}{2} =& \dfrac{56}{2} \\
n =& 28
\end{array}
$$

3. Multiply both sides of the equation by 10.

$$
10\left(6 + \dfrac{4}{5}b\right) = 10\left(\dfrac{9}{10}b\right)
$$

$$
\begin{array}{rl}
60 + 8b =& 9b \\
\underline{-8b} & \underline{-8b} \\
60 =& b
\end{array}
$$

4. Multiply both sides of the equation by 11.

$$
11\left(\dfrac{2}{11}m + 16\right) = 11\left(4 + \dfrac{6}{11}m\right)
$$

$$
\begin{array}{rl}
2m + 176 =& 44 + 6m \\
\underline{-2m} & \underline{-2m} \\
176 =& 44 + 4m \\
\underline{-44} & \underline{-44} \\
132 =& 4m \\
\dfrac{132}{4} =& \dfrac{4m}{4} \\
33 =& m
\end{array}
$$

5. Multiply both sides of the equation by 100.

$$
\begin{array}{rl}
100(2.25t + 5) =& 100(13.5t + 14) \\
225t + 500 =& 1{,}350t + 1{,}400 \\
\underline{-225t} & \underline{-225t} \\
500 =& 1{,}125t + 1{,}400 \\
\underline{-1{,}400} & \underline{-1{,}400} \\
-900 =& 1{,}125t \\
\dfrac{-900}{1{,}125} =& \dfrac{1{,}125t}{1{,}125} \\
-0.8 =& t
\end{array}
$$

6. Multiply both sides of the equation by 10.

$$
\begin{array}{rl}
10(3.6w) =& 10(1.6w + 24) \\
36w =& 16w + 240 \\
\underline{-16w} & \underline{-16w} \\
20w =& 240 \\
\dfrac{20w}{20} =& \dfrac{240}{20} \\
12 =& w
\end{array}
$$

7. Multiply both sides of the equation by 100.

$$100(-0.75p - 2) = 100(0.25p)$$

$$\begin{array}{rcl} -75p - 200 &=& 25p \\ +75p & & +75p \\ \hline -200 &=& 100p \end{array}$$

$$\frac{-200}{100} = \frac{100p}{100}$$

$$-2 = p$$

8. Sample answer: A store charges $1.25 per bathroom tile and lets you use their installation tools for free. Another store charges $0.75 per tile but charges you $50 to use their tools. How many tiles would you need to buy for the total cost to be the same?

9. The methods are essentially the same. The only extra step is that you begin solving by eliminating the fractions or the decimals from the equation.

## Independent Practice

10. Let $x$ represent the number of boat rentals.

$$105 + 9.50x = 14.75x$$

Multiply both sides of the equation by 100.

$$100(105 + 9.50x) = 100(14.75x)$$

$$\begin{array}{rcl} 10,500 + 950x &=& 1,475x \\ -950x & & -950x \\ \hline 10,500 &=& 525x \end{array}$$

$$\frac{10,500}{525} = \frac{525x}{525}$$

$$20 = x$$

They would pay the same amount for 20 boat rentals.

11. Let $x$ represent the number of tiles.

$$0.79x + 24 = 1.19x$$

Multiply both sides of the equation by 100.

$$100(0.79x + 24) = 100(1.19x)$$

$$\begin{array}{rcl} 79x + 2,400 &=& 119x \\ -79x & & -79x \\ \hline 2,400 &=& 40x \end{array}$$

$$\frac{2,400}{40} = \frac{40x}{40}$$

$$60 = x$$

The cost would be the same for 60 tiles.

12. Let $x$ represent the number of miles.

$$10 + 0.10x = 0.35x$$

Multiply both sides of the equation by 100.

$$100(10 + 0.10x) = 100(0.35x)$$

$$\begin{array}{rcl} 1,000 + 10x &=& 35x \\ -10x & & -10x \\ \hline 1,000 &=& 25x \end{array}$$

$$\frac{1,000}{25} = \frac{25x}{25}$$

$$40 = x$$

The cost would be the same for 40 miles.

13. a. Let $x$ represent the number of miles.

$$40 + 15 + 0.25x = 45 + 0.35x$$

$$55 + 0.25x = 45 + 0.35x$$

Multiply both sides of the equation by 100.

$$100(55 + 0.25x) = 100(45 + 0.35x)$$

$$\begin{array}{rcl} 5,500 + 25x &=& 4,500 + 35x \\ -25x & & -25x \\ \hline 5,500 &=& 4,500 + 10x \\ -4,500 & & -4,500 \\ \hline 1,000 &=& 10x \end{array}$$

$$\frac{1,000}{10} = \frac{10x}{10}$$

$$100 = x$$

The cost would be the same for 100 miles.

b. $55 + 0.25(100) = 45 + 0.35(100) = \$80$

The rental cost is $80.

14. Sample answer: $\frac{4}{5}x - 3 = \frac{3}{10}x + 7$

15. Sample answer: $0.4x - 5 = 0.08x + 3$

16. Use the formula $P = 2l + 2w$.

$$2(n + 0.6) + 2n = 2(n + 0.1) + 2(2n)$$

$$2n + 1.2 + 2n = 2n + 0.2 + 4n$$

$$4n + 1.2 = 6n + 0.2$$

$$10(4n + 1.2) = 10(6n + 0.2)$$

$$\begin{array}{rcl} 40n + 12 &=& 60n + 2 \\ -40n & & -40n \\ \hline 12 &=& 20n + 2 \\ -2 & & -2 \\ \hline 10 &=& 20n \end{array}$$

$$\frac{10}{20} = \frac{20n}{20}$$

$$0.5 = n$$

$P = 2l + 2w = 2(0.5) + 2(0.5 + 0.6) = 3.2$

The perimeter of each rectangle is 3.2 units.

17. The equation is $C = 1.8C + 32$.

$$C = 1.8C + 32$$

$$10(C) = 10(1.8C + 32)$$

$$\begin{array}{rcl} 10C &=& 18C + 320 \\ -18C & & -18C \\ \hline -8C &=& 320 \end{array}$$

$$\frac{-8C}{-8} = \frac{320}{-8}$$

$$C = -40$$

$-40°F = -40°C$

18. Agustin multiplied only the terms with fractional coefficients by the LCD. He should have multiplied all the terms. The correct answer is $x = -12$.

## Focus on Higher Order Thinking

19. Multiply both sides of the equation by 6.

$$6\left(\frac{1}{2}x - 5 + \frac{2}{3}x\right) = 6\left(\frac{7}{6}x + 4\right)$$

$$\begin{array}{rcl} 3x - 30 + 4x &=& 7x + 24 \\ 7x - 30 &=& 7x + 24 \\ -7x & & -7x \\ \hline -30 &=& 24 \end{array}$$

When you attempt to solve the equation, you eliminate the variable from both sides of the equation, leaving the false statement $-30 = 24$. Since the statement is false, the equation has no solution.

20. Each term on the left side of the equation is $\frac{1}{10}$ of the previous term. Since the pattern continues without end, the sum of the terms is 0.3333333…$x$, which equals $\frac{1}{3}x$. So, the equation is $\frac{1}{3}x = 3$, and the solution is $x = 9$.

21. No; the solution to his equation is $k = 3$, giving 3, 4, and 5 as the three integers. However, 3 and 5 are not even integers. He should have used the equation $k + (k + 2) + (k + 4) = 4k$, which gives $k = 6$ and the correct answer 6, 8, 10.

## LESSON 7.3

### Your Turn

1. 
$$y - 5 = 3 - 9(y + 2)$$
$$y - 5 = 3 - 9y - 18$$
$$y - 5 = -15 - 9y$$
$$\underline{\;+5\quad\;+5\;}$$
$$y = -10 - 9y$$
$$y = -10 - 9y$$
$$\underline{\;+9y\qquad\;+9y\;}$$
$$10y = -10$$
$$\frac{10y}{10} = \frac{-10}{10}$$
$$y = -1$$

2. 
$$2(x - 7) - 10 = 12 - 4x$$
$$2x - 14 - 10 = 12 - 4x$$
$$2x - 24 = 12 - 4x$$
$$\underline{\;+24\quad\;+24\;}$$
$$2x = 36 - 4x$$
$$2x = 36 - 4x$$
$$\underline{\;+4x\qquad\;+4x\;}$$
$$6x = 36$$
$$\frac{6x}{6} = \frac{36}{6}$$
$$x = 6$$

3. 
$$-4(-5 - b) = \frac{1}{3}(b + 16)$$
$$3 \times [-4(-5 - b)] = 3 \times \frac{1}{3}(b + 16)$$
$$-12(-5 - b) = b + 16$$
$$60 + 12b = b + 16$$
$$\underline{\;-60\qquad\;-60\;}$$
$$12b = b - 44$$
$$12b = b - 44$$
$$\underline{\;-b\quad\;-b\;}$$
$$11b = -44$$
$$\frac{11b}{11} = \frac{-44}{11}$$
$$b = -4$$

4. 
$$\frac{3}{5}(t + 18) = -3(2 - t)$$
$$\frac{5}{3} \times \frac{3}{5}(t + 18) = \frac{5}{3} \times [-3(2 - t)]$$
$$t + 18 = -5(2 - t)$$
$$t + 18 = -10 + 5t$$
$$\underline{\;-18\qquad\quad\;-18\;}$$
$$t = -28 + 5t$$
$$t = -28 + 5t$$
$$\underline{\;-5t\qquad\;-5t\;}$$
$$-4t = -28$$
$$\frac{-4t}{-4} = \frac{-28}{-4}$$
$$t = 7$$

5. 
$$0.08(x + 2,000) = 3,840$$
$$0.08x + 160 = 3,840$$
$$\underline{\;-160\qquad\;-160\;}$$
$$0.08x = 3,680$$
$$\frac{0.08x}{0.08} = \frac{3,680}{0.08}$$
$$x = 46,000$$

The Smiths' total family budget last year was $46,000.

### Guided Practice

1. 
$$4(x + 8) - 4 = 34 - 2x$$
$$4x + 32 - 4 = 34 - 2x$$
$$4x + 28 = 34 - 2x$$
$$6x + 28 = 34$$
$$6x = 6$$
$$\frac{6x}{6} = \frac{6}{6}$$
$$x = 1$$

2. 
$$\frac{2}{3}(9 + x) = -5(4 - x)$$
$$3 \times \frac{2}{3}(9 + x) = 3 \times [-5(4 - x)]$$
$$2(9 + x) = -15(4 - x)$$
$$18 + 2x = -60 + 15x$$
$$-13x = -78$$
$$\frac{-13x}{-13} = \frac{-78}{-13}$$
$$x = 6$$

3. 
$$-3(x + 4) + 15 = 6 - 4x$$
$$-3x - 12 + 15 = 6 - 4x$$
$$-3x + 3 = 6 - 4x$$
$$\underline{\;-3\qquad\;-3\;}$$
$$-3x = 3 - 4x$$
$$-3x = 3 - 4x$$
$$\underline{\;+4x\qquad\;+4x\;}$$
$$x = 3$$

4. $10 + 4x = 5(x - 6) + 33$
$10 + 4x = 5x - 30 + 33$
$10 + 4x = 5x + 3$
$\underline{-10 \qquad\quad -10}$
$4x = 5x - 7$
$4x = \quad 5x - 7$
$\underline{-5x \quad -5x}$
$-x = \qquad -7$
$\dfrac{-x}{-1} = \dfrac{-7}{-1}$
$x = 7$

5. $x - 9 = 8(2x + 3) - 18$
$x - 9 = 16x + 24 - 18$
$x - 9 = 16x + 6$
$\underline{+9 \qquad\quad +9}$
$x = 16x + 15$
$x = \quad 16x + 15$
$\underline{-16x \quad -16x}$
$-15x = \qquad 15$
$\dfrac{-15x}{-15} = \dfrac{15}{-15}$
$x = -1$

6. $-6(x - 1) - 7 = -7x + 2$
$-6x + 6 - 7 = -7x + 2$
$-6x - 1 = -7x + 2$
$\underline{+1 \qquad\qquad +1}$
$-6x = -7x + 3$
$-6x = -7x + 3$
$\underline{+7x \quad +7x}$
$x = \qquad 3$
$x = 3$

7. $\dfrac{1}{10}(x + 11) = -2(8 - x)$
$10 \times \dfrac{1}{10}(x + 11) = 10 \times [-2(8 - x)]$
$x + 11 = -20(8 - x)$
$x + 11 = -160 + 20x$
$\underline{-11 \qquad -11}$
$x = -171 + 20x$
$x = -171 + 20x$
$\underline{-20x \qquad\quad -20x}$
$-19x = -171$
$\dfrac{-19x}{-19} = \dfrac{-171}{-19}$
$x = 9$

8. $-(4 - x) = \dfrac{3}{4}(x - 6)$
$4 \times [-(4 - x)] = 4 \times \dfrac{3}{4}(x - 6)$
$-4(4 - x) = 3(x - 6)$
$-16 + 4x = 3x - 18$
$\underline{+16 \qquad\qquad +16}$
$4x = 3x - 2$
$4x = \quad 3x - 2$
$\underline{-3x \quad -3x}$
$x = \qquad -2$
$x = -2$

9. $-8(8 - x) = \dfrac{4}{5}(x + 10)$
$5 \times [-8(8 - x)] = 5 \times \dfrac{4}{5}(x + 10)$
$-40(8 - x) = 4(x + 10)$
$-320 + 40x = 4x + 40$
$\underline{+320 \qquad\qquad +320}$
$40x = 4x + 360$
$40x = \quad 4x + 360$
$\underline{-4x \qquad -4x}$
$36x = \qquad 360$
$\dfrac{36x}{36} = \dfrac{360}{36}$
$x = 10$

10. $\dfrac{1}{2}(16 - x) = -12(x + 7)$
$2 \times \dfrac{1}{2}(16 - x) = 2 \times [-12(x + 7)]$
$16 - x = -24(x + 7)$
$16 - x = -24x - 168$
$\underline{-16 \qquad\qquad -16}$
$-x = -24x - 184$
$-x = -24x - 184$
$\underline{+24x \quad +24x}$
$23x = \qquad -184$
$\dfrac{23x}{23} = \dfrac{-184}{23}$
$x = -8$

11. $0.12(x + 3{,}000) = 4{,}200$
$0.12(x + 3{,}000) = 4{,}200$
$0.12x + 360 = 4.200$
$\underline{-360 \qquad -360}$
$0.12x = 3{,}840$
$\dfrac{0.12x}{0.12} = \dfrac{3{,}840}{0.12}$
$x = 32{,}000$
Write an equation. $0.12(x + 3{,}000) = 4{,}200$
Sandra's salary the previous year was $32,000.

12. Sample answer: You eliminate the fractions by using their LCD. The resulting computations will be less complicated without fractions.

### Independent Practice

13. a. Martina is currently 14 years older than her cousin Joey, and Joey is currently $x$ years old. To find Martina's current age, add 14 to Joey's current age. Martina's current age can be expressed as $x + 14$.

   b. Joey's current age is $x$, and Martina's current age is $x + 14$. To find the ages of Joey and Martina in 5 years, add 5 to both of their current ages. Joey's age in 5 years can be expressed as $x + 5$, and Martina's age in 5 years can be expressed as $x + 14 + 5 = x + 19$.

   c. Joey's age in 5 years will be $x + 5$, and Martina's age in 5 years will be $x + 19$. 1n 5 years, Martina will be 3 times as old as Joey. The equation you can write based on the information given is $3(x + 5) = x + 19$.

d. $3(x + 5) = x + 19$
$3x + 15 = x + 19$
$\underline{\phantom{3x}-15 \phantom{xxx}-15}$
$3x \phantom{xx} = x + 4$
$3x = x + 4$
$\underline{-x \phantom{xxx}-x}$
$2x = \phantom{xxxx} 4$
$\dfrac{2x}{2} = \dfrac{4}{2}$
$x = 2$
$2 + 14 = 16$

Joey is currently 2 years old, and Martina is currently 16 years old.

14. $4(x - 5) + 7 = 35$
$4x - 20 + 7 = 35$
$4x - 13 = \phantom{xx} 35$
$\underline{\phantom{4x} + 13 = + \phantom{x}13}$
$4x \phantom{xx} = \phantom{xx} 48$
$4x = 48$
$\dfrac{4x}{4} = \dfrac{48}{4}$
$x = 12$

The equation Luis can write based on Sarah's clues is $4(x - 5) + 7 = 35$. Sarah's number is 12.

15. On the left side of the equation, multiplying 4 and 6 by $\frac{1}{2}$ gives 2 and 3. On the right side of the equation, multiplying 9 and $-24$ by $\frac{1}{3}$ gives 3 and $-8$. It is not necessary. In this case, distributing the fractions directly results in whole number coefficients and constants.

16. $\frac{1}{2}(4x + 6) = \frac{1}{3}(9x - 24)$
$6 \times \frac{1}{2}(4x + 6) = 6 \times \frac{1}{3}(9x - 24)$
$3(4x + 6) = 2(9x - 24)$
$12x + 18 = 18x - 48$
$\underline{\phantom{12x}-18 \phantom{xxxx}-18}$
$12x \phantom{x} = 18x - 66$
$12x = \phantom{x}18x - 66$
$\underline{-18x \phantom{x}-18x}$
$-6x = \phantom{xxxx}-66$
$\dfrac{-6x}{-6} = \dfrac{-66}{-6}$
$x = 11$

$\frac{1}{2}(4x + 6) = \frac{1}{3}(9x - 24)$
$2x + 3 = 3x - 8$
$\underline{\phantom{2x}-3 \phantom{xxx}-3}$
$2x \phantom{xx} = 3x - 11$
$2x = \phantom{x}3x - 11$
$\underline{-3x \phantom{x}-3x}$
$-x = \phantom{xxxx}-11$
$\dfrac{-x}{-1} = \dfrac{-11}{-1}$
$x = 11$

Yes, the answers are the same. Using either method gives $x = 11$.

17. The number of milliliters of the 15% solution is equal to the number of milliliters of the mixture minus the number of milliliters of the 25% solution. Also, the number of milliliters of acid in each solution is equal to the number of milliliters of the solution times the percent acid written as a decimal.

| | ml of Solution | Percent Acid as a Decimal | ml of Acid |
|---|---|---|---|
| 25% Solution | $x$ | 0.25 | $0.25x$ |
| 15% Solution | $100 - x$ | 0.15 | $0.15(100 - x)$ |
| Mixture (19% Solution) | 100 | 0.19 | $0.19(100) = 19$ |

a. The 25% solution is being added to the 15% solution to produce the 19% mixture. The milliliters of acid in the 25% solution plus the milliliters of acid in the 15% solution equals the milliliters of acid in the mixture.

b. There are $0.25x$ milliliters of acid in the 25% solution, $0.15(100 - x)$ milliliters of acid in the 15% solution, and 19 milliliters of acid in the mixture. The equation that you can use to solve for $x$ based on your answer to part a is $0.25x + 0.15(100 - x) = 19$.

c. $0.25x + 0.15(100 - x) = 19$
$0.25x + 15 - 0.15x = 19$
$0.1x + 15 = \phantom{xx} 19$
$\underline{\phantom{0.1x}-15 \phantom{xxx}-15}$
$0.1x \phantom{xx} = \phantom{xx} 4$
$0.1x = 4$
$\dfrac{0.1x}{0.1} = \dfrac{4}{0.1}$
$x = 40$
$100 - 40 = 60$

The chemist used 40 milliliters of the 25% solution and 60 milliliters of the 15% solution.

**Focus on Higher Order Thinking**

18. $5(2x) - 3 = 20x + 15$
$10x - 3 = 20x + 15$
$\underline{\phantom{10x}+ 3 \phantom{xxx}+ 3}$
$10x \phantom{xx} = 20x + 18$
$10x = \phantom{x}20x + 18$
$\underline{-20x \phantom{x}-20x}$
$-10x = \phantom{xxxx}18$
$-10x = 18$
$\dfrac{-10x}{-10} = \dfrac{18}{-10}$
$x = -1.8$

Anne did not need to use the Distributive Property. The parentheses are only around $2x$ and are used to represent $5 \cdot 2x$, not $5(2x - 3)$. The correct answer is $x = -1.8$.

19. $5[3(x + 4) - 2(1 - x)] - x - 15 = 14x + 45$

$\qquad 5[3x + 12 - 2 + 2x] - x - 15 = 14x + 45$

$\qquad\quad 5[5x + 10] - x - 15 = 14x + 45$

$\qquad\quad 25x + 50 - x - 15 = 14x + 45$

$\qquad\qquad\qquad 24x + 35 = 14x + 45$

$\qquad\qquad\qquad\quad\underline{-\ 35 \qquad\qquad -\ 35}$

$\qquad\qquad\qquad\quad 24x \qquad = 14x + 10$

$\qquad\qquad\qquad\quad 24x = \quad 14x + 10$

$\qquad\qquad\qquad\quad\underline{-\ 14x \quad -\ 14x}$

$\qquad\qquad\qquad\qquad 10x = \qquad\quad 10$

$\qquad\qquad\qquad\qquad 10x = 10$

$\qquad\qquad\qquad\qquad \dfrac{10x}{10} = \dfrac{10}{10}$

$\qquad\qquad\qquad\qquad\quad x = 1$

Sample answer: Use the Distributive Property to distribute both 3 and 2 inside the square parentheses on the left side. Combine like terms inside the square parentheses. Then use the Distributive Property again to distribute 5. Combine like terms on the left side and use inverse operations to solve the equation. The solution is $x = 1$.

## LESSON 7.4

### Your Turn

2. $2x + 1 = 5x - 8$

$\quad\underline{-1 \qquad\ -1}$

$2x \quad\ = 5x - 9$

$\qquad 2x = \quad 5x - 9$

$\qquad\underline{-5x \quad -5x}$

$\qquad -3x = \quad -9$

$\qquad \dfrac{-3x}{-3} = \dfrac{-9}{-3}$

$\qquad\quad x = 3$

The final equation is a true statement.

3. $3(4x + 3) - 2 = 12x + 7$

$\quad 12x + 9 - 2 = 12x + 7$

$\qquad 12x + 7 = \quad 12x + 7$

$\qquad\underline{-12x \qquad = -12x}$

$\qquad\qquad\quad 7 = \qquad 7$

The final equation is a true statement.

4. $\quad 3x - 9 = 5 + 3x$

$\quad\underline{-3x \qquad\quad -3x}$

$\qquad -9 = 5$

The final equation is a false statement.

6. $\quad 6 + 3x = x - 8$

$\quad\underline{-6 \qquad\quad -6}$

$\qquad 3x = x - 14$

$\qquad 3x = x - 14$

$\qquad\underline{-x \quad -x}$

$\qquad 2x = -14$

$\qquad \dfrac{2x}{2} = \dfrac{-14}{2}$

$\qquad\ x = -7$

The equation has one solution.

7. $\quad 8x + 4 = 4(2x + 1)$

$\qquad 8x + 4 = \quad 8x + 4$

$\qquad\underline{-8x \quad = -8x}$

$\qquad\qquad 4 = \qquad 4$

The equation has infinitely many solutions.

8. $\quad 3x + 1 = \quad 3x + 6$

$\quad\underline{-3x \qquad -3x}$

$\qquad 1 = \qquad 6$

Sample answer: 6

Any number except 1 will yield no solution.

9. $\quad 2x - 4 = \quad 2x - 4$

$\quad\underline{-2x \qquad -2x}$

$\quad -4 = \qquad -4$

4

### Guided Practice

1. $\quad 3x - 2 = 25 - 6x$

$\quad\underline{+6x \qquad\ +6x}$

$\quad 9x - 2 = 25$

$\quad\underline{\quad +2 \quad +2}$

$\quad 9x \quad\ = 27$

$\qquad \dfrac{9x}{9} = \dfrac{27}{9}$

$\qquad\ x = 3$

The statement is true.

2. $\quad 2x - 4 = 2(x - 1) + 3$

$\quad 2x - 4 = 2x - 2 + 3$

$\quad 2x - 4 = \quad 2x + 1$

$\quad\underline{-2x \qquad\ -2x}$

$\qquad -4 = \quad 1$

The statement is false.

3. The equation in Exercise 2 was transformed into $a = b$, where $a$ and $b$ are different numbers. There is no value of $x$ that makes the equation a true statement. There are no solutions to the equation in Exercise 2.

4. Sample answer: The equation was transformed into $a = a$, where $a$ is a number. Any value of $x$ makes the equation a true statement. The equation has infinitely many solutions.

5. To write an equation in one variable that has infinitely many solutions, do the following.

| Start with a true statement. | $10 = 10$ |
|---|---|
| Add the same variable to both sides. | $10 + x = 10 + x$ |
| Add the same constant to both sides. | $10 + x + 5 = 10 + x + 5$ |
| Combine like terms. | $15 + x = 15 + x$ |

6. Infinite number of solutions:

$\quad 2x + 1 = \quad 2x + 1$

$\quad\underline{-2x \qquad\ -2x}$

$\qquad 1 = \qquad 1$

No solution:

$\quad 2x + 1 = \quad 2x$

$\quad\underline{-2x \qquad -2x}$

$\qquad 1 = \quad 0$

Sample answer: An equation with an infinite number of solutions is $2x + 1 = 2x + 1$. When the equation is changed to $2x + 1 = 2x$, it has no solutions.

## Independent Practice

7. $-(2x + 2) - 1 = -x - (x + 3)$
$-2x - 2 - 1 = -x - x - 3$
$-2x - 3 = -2x - 3$
$\underline{+2x \qquad\quad +2x}$
$-3 = \qquad -3$

The equation has infinitely many solutions.

8. $-2(z + 3) - z = -z - 4(z + 2)$
$-2z - 6 - z = -z - 4z - 8$
$-3z - 6 = -5z - 8$
$\underline{+6 \qquad\quad +6}$
$-3z \qquad = -5z - 2$
$-3z = -5z - 2$
$\underline{+5z \qquad +5z}$
$2z = \qquad -2$
$\dfrac{2z}{2} = \dfrac{-2}{2}$
$z = -1$

The equation has one solution.

9. The number can be any number except $-4$.

$3\left(x - \dfrac{4}{3}\right) = 3x + 5$
$3x - 4 = \quad 3x + 5$
$\underline{-3x \qquad -3x}$
$-4 = \qquad 5$

Sample answer: $3\left(x - \dfrac{4}{3}\right) = 3x + 5$

10. $2(x - 1) + 6x = 4(2x - 1) + 2$
$2x - 2 + 6x = 8x - 4 + 2$
$8x - 2 = \quad 8x - 2$
$\underline{-8x \qquad\quad -8x}$
$-2 = \qquad -2$
$2(x - 1) + 6x = 4(2x - 1) + 2$

11. $5x - (x - 2) = 2x - (x + 1)$
$5x - x + 2 = 2x - x - 1$
$4x + 2 = x - 1$
$\underline{-2 \qquad\quad -2}$
$4x \quad = x - 3$
$4x = \quad x - 3$
$\underline{-x \qquad -x}$
$3x = -3$
$\dfrac{3x}{3} = \dfrac{-3}{3}$
$x = -1$
$5x - (x - 2) = 2x - (x + 1)$

12. $-(x - 8) + 4x = 2(x + 4) + x$
$-x + 8 + 4x = 2x + 8 + x$
$3x + 8 = \quad 3x + 8$
$\underline{-3x \qquad\quad -3x}$
$8 = \qquad 8$
$-(x - 8) + 4x = 2(x + 4) + x$

13. a. $(2x - 2) + (x + 1) + x + (x + 1)$
$\qquad = (2x - 9) + (x + 1) + (x + 8) + x$
$\qquad\quad 5x = 5x$
$\qquad\quad \underline{-5x \quad -5x}$
$\qquad\qquad 0 = 0$

Yes, there is more than one value of $x$. Because the perimeters are equal, you get the equation $(2x - 2) + (x + 1) + x + (x + 1) = (2x - 9) + (x + 1) + (x + 8) + x$, or $5x = 5x$. When $5x$ is subtracted from both sides of the equation, you get $0 = 0$, which is a true statement in the form $a = a$, where a is a number, so there are an infinite number of values for $x$.

b. Sample answer: The condition was that the two perimeters are to be equal. However, a specific number was not given, so there are an infinite number of possible perimeters.

c. Trapezoid:
$(2x - 2) + (x + 1) + x + (x + 1) = 60$
$\qquad\qquad\qquad\qquad\quad 5x = 60$
$\qquad\qquad\qquad\qquad \dfrac{5x}{5} = \dfrac{60}{5}$
$\qquad\qquad\qquad\qquad\quad x = 12$

Quadrilateral:
$(2x - 9) + (x + 1) + (x + 8) + x = 60$
$\qquad\qquad\qquad\qquad\qquad 5x = 60$
$\qquad\qquad\qquad\qquad \dfrac{5x}{5} = \dfrac{60}{5}$
$\qquad\qquad\qquad\qquad\quad x = 12$

The value of $x$ in this case is 12; Sample answer: I used the trapezoid and wrote the equation $(2x - 2) + (x + 1) + x + (x + 1) = 60$. Solving this gives $x = 12$.

14. $9x - 25 + x = x + 50 + 2x - 12$
$10x - 25 = 3x + 38$
$\underline{+25 \qquad\quad +25}$
$10x \qquad = 3x + 63$
$10x = \quad 3x + 63$
$\underline{-3x \quad -3x}$
$7x = \qquad 63$
$\dfrac{7x}{7} = \dfrac{63}{7}$
$x = 9$

Left angle:
$9x - 25 + x$
$= 9(9) - 25 + 9$
$= 81 - 25 + 9$
$= 65$

Right angle:
$x + 50 + 2x - 12$
$= 9 + 50 + 2(9) - 12$
$= 9 + 50 + 18 - 12$
$= 65$

I agree with Marta. If the angles have the same measure, $9x - 25 + x = x + 50 + 2x - 12$. Solving this equation gives a single solution, $x = 9$. Since $9(9) - 25 + 9 = 81 - 25 + 9 = 65$ and $9 + 50 + 2(9) - 12 = 9 + 50 + 18 - 12 = 65$, each angle measures $65°$.

15. Let $x$ equal the number of months.
$100 + 35x = 50 + 35x$
$\underline{-35x = \qquad -35x}$
$100 \qquad = 50$

No, Adele and Kent will not have the same amount in their accounts at any point. Letting $x$ equal the number of months and setting the expressions $100 + 35x$ and $50 + 35x$ equal to each other and solving for $x$ gives $100 = 50$, which is false and in the form $a = b$, where a and b are different numbers. Therefore, the equation has no solution.

## Focus on Higher Order Thinking

16. Frank:
$$x + 12 = x + 12$$
$$\underline{\quad -12 \qquad -12\quad}$$
$$x \quad\;\; = x$$

Sarah:
$$x + 12 = \quad x + 12$$
$$\underline{-x \qquad\quad -x\quad}$$
$$12 = \qquad 12$$

The results may appear different, but their meaning is the same. Both are true statements, so the equation has infinitely many solutions. Frank solved the equation by eliminating 12, while Sarah eliminated $x$.

17. 
$$2x - 7 = 2(x - 7)$$
$$2x - 7 = \quad 2x - 14$$
$$\underline{-2x \quad\;\; = -2x\quad}$$
$$-7 = \qquad -14$$

Matt is incorrect. Sample answer: He applied the Distributive Property to the right side incorrectly. Correctly simplified, the equation is $-7 = -14$, which is false because it is in the form $a = b$, where $a$ and $b$ are two different numbers. This means that there is no solution.

## MODULE 7

### Ready to Go On?

1. 
$$4a - 4 = \quad 8 + a$$
$$\underline{-a \qquad\qquad -a\quad}$$
$$3a - 4 = \quad 8$$
$$\underline{\;+4 \qquad +4\quad}$$
$$3a = 12$$
$$\frac{3a}{3} = \frac{12}{3}$$
$$a = 4$$

2. 
$$4x + 5 = \quad x + 8$$
$$\underline{-x \qquad\quad -x\quad}$$
$$3x + 5 = \quad 8$$
$$\underline{\;-5 \qquad -5\quad}$$
$$3x = \quad 3$$
$$\frac{3x}{3} = \frac{3}{3}$$
$$x = \quad 1$$

3. Let $x$ represent the number of chairs in each row.
$$6c + 3 = 8c - 11$$
$$6c + 3 + 11 = 8c - 11 + 11$$
$$6c + 14 = \quad 8c$$
$$\underline{-6c \qquad\quad -6c\quad}$$
$$14 = \quad 2c$$
$$\frac{14}{2} = \frac{2c}{2}$$
$$7 = c$$

There are 7 chairs in each row.

4. Multiply both sides of the equation by 6.
$$6\left(\frac{2}{3}n - \frac{2}{3}\right) = 6\left(\frac{n}{6} + \frac{4}{3}\right)$$
$$4n - 4 = \quad n + 8$$
$$\underline{-n \qquad\qquad -n\quad}$$
$$3n - 4 = \quad 8$$
$$\underline{\;+4 \qquad +4\quad}$$
$$3n = 12$$
$$\frac{3n}{3} = \frac{12}{3}$$
$$n = 4$$

5. Multiply both sides of the equation by 100.
$$100(1.5d + 3.25) = 100(1 + 2.25d)$$
$$150d + 325 = \quad 100 + 225d$$
$$\underline{-150d \qquad\qquad -150d\quad}$$
$$325 = \quad 100 + 75d$$
$$\underline{-100 \qquad -100\quad}$$
$$225 = 75d$$
$$\frac{225}{75} = \frac{75d}{75}$$
$$3 = d$$

6. Let $h$ represent the number of hours.
$$19.00 + 1.50h = 14.00 + 2.75h$$
Multiply both sides of the equation by 100.
$$100(19.00 + 1.50h) = 100(14.00 + 2.75h)$$
$$1{,}900 + 150h = \quad 1{,}400 + 275h$$
$$\underline{-150h \qquad\qquad -150h\quad}$$
$$1{,}900 = \quad 1{,}400 + 125h$$
$$\underline{-1{,}400 \qquad -1{,}400\quad}$$
$$500 = 125h$$
$$\frac{500}{125} = \frac{125h}{125}$$
$$4 = h$$

The cost would be the same for 4 hours.

7. 
$$14 + 5x = 3(-x + 3) - 11$$
$$14 + 5x = -3x + 9 - 11$$
$$14 + 5x = -3x - 2$$
$$\underline{-14 \qquad\qquad -14\quad}$$
$$5x = -3x - 16$$
$$\underline{+3x \quad +3x\quad}$$
$$8x = -16$$
$$\frac{8x}{8} = \frac{-16}{8}$$
$$x = -2$$

8. 
$$\frac{1}{4}(x - 7) = 1 + 3x$$
$$4 \times \left[\frac{1}{4}(x - 7)\right] = 4 \times [1 + 3x]$$
$$x - 7 = 4 + 12x$$
$$\underline{-4 \qquad -4\quad}$$
$$x - 11 = 12x$$
$$\underline{-x \qquad\quad -x\quad}$$
$$-11 = 11x$$
$$\underline{-11 \qquad 11x\quad}$$
$$11 = 11$$
$$x = -1$$

9. $-5(2x - 9) = 2(x - 8) - 11$
$-10x + 45 = 2x - 16 - 11$
$-10x + 45 = 2x - 27$

$$\begin{array}{r} \underline{+27 \qquad +27} \\ -10x + 72 = 2x \\ \underline{+10x \qquad +10x} \\ 72 = 12x \end{array}$$

$$\frac{72}{12} = \frac{12x}{12}$$
$$x = 6$$

10. $3(x + 5) = 2(3x + 12)$
$3x + 15 = 6x + 24$

$$\begin{array}{r} \underline{-24 \qquad -24} \\ 3x - 9 = 6x \\ \underline{-3x \qquad -3x} \\ -9 = 3x \end{array}$$

$$\frac{-9}{3} = \frac{3x}{3}$$
$$x = -3$$

11. $5(x - 3) + 6 = 5x - 9$
$5x - 15 + 6 = 5x - 9$
$5x - 9 = 5x - 9$

$$\begin{array}{r} \underline{-5x \qquad -5x} \\ -9 = -9 \end{array}$$

The equation $-9 = -9$ is true, so the original equation has infinitely many solutions.

12. $5(x - 3) + 6 = 5x - 10$
$5x - 15 + 6 = 5x - 10$
$5x - 9 = 5x - 10$

$$\begin{array}{r} \underline{-5x \qquad -5x} \\ -9 = -10 \end{array}$$

The equation $-9 = -10$ is false, so the original equation has zero solutions.

13. $5(x - 3) + 6 = 4x + 3$
$5x - 15 + 6 = 4x + 3$
$5x - 9 = 4x + 3$

$$\begin{array}{r} \underline{-5x \qquad -5x} \\ -9 = -x + 3 \\ \underline{-3 \qquad -3} \\ -12 = -x \\ x = 12 \end{array}$$

The equation has one solution.

## MODULE 8 *Solving Systems of Linear Equations*

### Are You Ready?

1. $14x - 4x + 21$
   $10x + 21$

2. $-y - 4x + 4y$
   $-y + 4y - 4x$
   $3y - 4x$

3. $5.5a - 1 + 21b + 3a$
   $5.5a + 3a + 21b - 1$
   $8.5a + 21b - 1$

4. $2y - 3x + 6x - y$
   $2y - y - 3x + 6x$
   $y + 3x$

5. $y = 4x - 1$
   Plot $(0, -1)$ and $(1, 3)$.

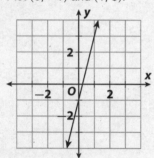

6. $y = \frac{1}{2}x + 1$
   Plot $(0, 1)$ and $(2, 2)$.

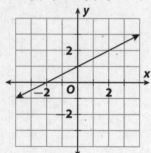

7. $y = -x$
   Plot $(0, 0)$ and $(2, -2)$.

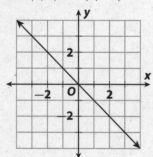

## LESSON 8.1

### Your Turn

3.

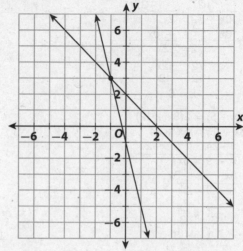

The solution is the point of intersection: $(-1, 3)$.
Check:

$y = -x + 2$ 　　　　　 $y = -4x - 1$

$3 \overset{?}{=} -(-1) + 2$ 　　 $3 \overset{?}{=} -4(-1) - 1$
$3 = 3$ ✓ 　　　　　 $3 = 3$ ✓

4.

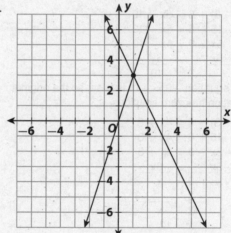

The solution is the point of intersection: $(1, 3)$.
Check:

$y = -2x + 5$ 　　　　 $y = 3x$

$3 \overset{?}{=} -2(1) + 5$ 　 $3 \overset{?}{=} 3(1)$
$3 = 3$ ✓ 　　　　 $3 = 3$ ✓

6. a. Since he wants to play a total of 6 games,
   $x + y = 6$. Since each game of bowling costs $2,
   and each game of laser tag costs $4, and he
   wants to spend exactly $20, $2x + 4y = 20$.

   $x + y = 6$ 　　　　 $2x + 4y = 20$
   　　$y = -x + 6$ 　　　 $4y = -2x + 20$
   　　　　　　　　　　　 $y = -\frac{1}{2}x + 5$

In slope-intercept form, the system of equations is
$$\begin{cases} y = -x + 6 \\ y = -\frac{1}{2}x + 5 \end{cases}$$

b.

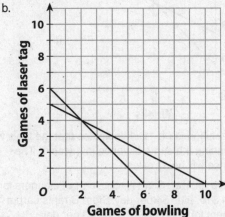

**Games of bowling** (x-axis), **Games of laser tag** (y-axis)

c. The solution is the point of intersection: (2, 4). Marquis will bowl 2 games and play 4 games of laser tag.

## Guided Practice

1.

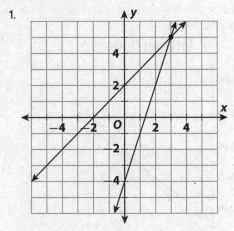

The solution is the point of intersection: (3, 5).

2.

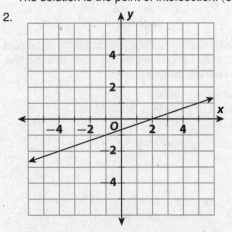

Since the equations represent the same line, there are infinitely many solutions.

3. a. Since there is a total of 15 questions, $x + y = 15$. Solve the equation for $y$.
$$x + y = 15$$
$$y = -x + 15$$

b. Since spelling questions are worth 5 points and vocabulary questions are worth 10 points, and since the maximum number of points possible is 100, $5x + 10y = 100$. Solve the equation for $y$.

$$5x + 10y = 100$$
$$10y = -5x + 100$$
$$y = -\frac{1}{2}x + 10$$

c.

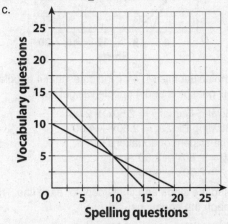

**Spelling questions** (x-axis), **Vocabulary questions** (y-axis)

d. The solution is the point of intersection: (10, 5). There are 10 spelling questions and 5 vocabulary questions.

4. Every point on a line represents a solution of the equation of the line. The point of intersection represents a solution of both equations.

## Independent Practice

5. A system of equations is a set of equations that have the same variables.

6. a. Since there is a total of 8 people, and each will wear either a shirt or a cap, $x + y = 8$. Since shirts cost $6 each and caps cost $3 each, and since they want to spend $36, $6x + 3y = 36$. The system of equations is
$$\begin{cases} x + y = 8 \\ 6x + 3y = 36 \end{cases}$$

b. Write each equation in slope intercept form. Then graph the lines.

$$x + y = 8 \qquad\qquad 6x + 3y = 36$$
$$y = -x + 8 \qquad\qquad 3y = -6x + 36$$
$$\qquad\qquad\qquad\qquad y = -2x + 12$$

## Business Logo Wear

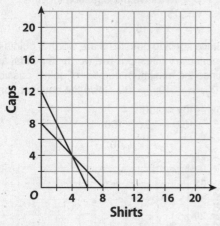

The solution is (4, 4). It indicates that 4 people will get shirts and 4 people will get caps.

7. a. Bowl-o-Rama: $y = 2.50x + 2.00$
Bowling Pinz: $y = 2.00x + 4.00$
The system of equations is
$$\begin{cases} y = 2.50x + 2.00 \\ y = 2.00x + 4.00 \end{cases}$$

b. Find the slope and $y$-intercept for each line. Then graph the equations.

Bowl-o-Rama: $m = 2.50 = \frac{5}{2}$, $b = 2$

Bowling Pinz: $m = 2 = \frac{2}{1}$, $b = 4$

### Cost of Bowling

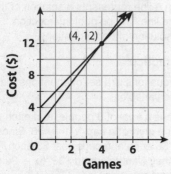

The solution is (4, 12). It indicates that the cost at both bowling alleys will be the same when 4 games are bowled. The cost will be $12.

8. Let $x$ = number of weeks
Let $y$ = number of miles
Jeremy: $y = x + 7$
Tony: $y = 2x + 3$
Graph the equations.

## Running Distance

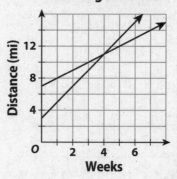

The solution is (4, 11). It indicates that the boys will be running the same distance in 4 weeks. The distance will be 11 miles.

9. Sample answer: Store A rents carpet cleaners for a fee of $10, plus $4 per day. Store B rents carpet cleaners for a fee of $15, plus $3 per day.

**Focus on Higher Order Thinking**

10. a. Let $x$ = number of months
Let $y$ = total cost
Option 1: $y = 30x + 50$
Option 2: $y = 40x$
Graph the equations.

### Internet Options

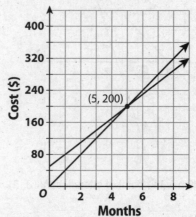

The solution is (5, 200). It indicates that the cost for the two options will be the same in 5 months. The cost will be $200.

b. Option 1 is cheaper;
Option 1: $y = 30(9) + 50 = \$320$
Option 2: $y = 40(9) = \$360$

11. Solve each equation for $y$.
$x - y = 3$
$-y = -x + 3$
$y = x - 3$
$ay - ax + 3a = 0$
$ay = ax - 3a$
$y = x - 3$

Since the equations represent the same line, there are infinitely many solutions.

# LESSON 8.2

**Your Turn**

4. Solve an equation for one variable.

$-2x + y = 1$

$\qquad y = 2x + 1$

Substitute the expression for $y$ in the other equation and solve.

$\qquad 3x + y = 11$

$3x + (2x + 1) = 11$

$\qquad 5x + 1 = 11$

$\qquad 5x = 10$

$\qquad x = 2$

Substitute the value for $x$ into one of the equations and solve for $y$.

$-2x + y = 1$

$-2(2) + y = 1$

$-4 + y = 1$

$\qquad y = 5$

So, the solution of the system is $(2, 5)$.

5. Solve an equation for one variable.

$x + 6y = 18$

$\qquad x = 18 - 6y$

Substitute the expression for $x$ in the other equation and solve.

$\qquad 2x - 3y = -24$

$2(18 - 6y) - 3y = -24$

$36 - 12y - 3y = -24$

$\qquad 36 - 15y = -24$

$\qquad 60 = 15y$

$\qquad 4 = y$

Substitute the value for $y$ into one of the equations and solve for $x$.

$x + 6y = 18$

$x + 6(4) = 18$

$x + 24 = 18$

$\qquad x = -6$

So, the solution of the system is $(-6, 4)$.

6. Solve an equation for one variable.

$x - 2y = 5$

$\qquad x = 5 + 2y$

Substitute the expression for $x$ in the other equation and solve.

$\qquad 3x - 5y = 8$

$3(5 + 2y) - 5y = 8$

$15 + 6y - 5y = 8$

$\qquad 15 + y = 8$

$\qquad y = -7$

Substitute the value for $y$ into one of the equations and solve for $x$.

$x - 2y = 5$

$x - 2(-7) = 5$

$x + 14 = 5$

$\qquad x = -9$

So, the solution of the system is $(-9, -7)$.

7. Sketch a graph of each equation by substituting values for $x$ and generating values of $y$.

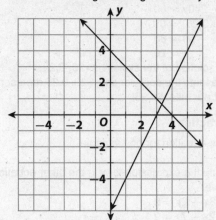

Find the intersection of the lines. The lines appear to intersect near $(3, 1)$.

The estimated solution is $(3, 1)$.

Solve the system of equations.

Solve an equation for one variable.

$x + y = 4$

$\qquad x = 4 - y$

Substitute the expression for $x$ in the other equation and solve.

$\qquad 2x - y = 6$

$2(4 - y) - y = 6$

$\qquad 8 - 2y - y = 6$

$\qquad 8 - 3y = 6$

$\qquad -3y = -2$

$\qquad y = \dfrac{2}{3}$

Substitute the value for $y$ into one the equations and solve for $x$.

$x + y = 4$

$x + \dfrac{2}{3} = 4$

$\qquad x = 3\dfrac{1}{3} = \dfrac{10}{3}$

The algebraic solution is $\left(\dfrac{10}{3}, \dfrac{2}{3}\right)$.

The solution is reasonable because $\dfrac{10}{3}$ is close to the estimate of 3, and $\dfrac{2}{3}$ is close to the estimate of 1.

8. Write the equation to represent Carlos' expenses.

Carlos: $4x + 160y = 120$

Write the equation to represent Vanessa's expenses.

Vanessa: $x + 240y = 80$

Solve an equation for one variable.

$x + 240y = 80$

$\qquad x = 80 - 240y$

Substitute the expression for $x$ in the other equation and solve.

$4(80 - 240y) + 160y = 120$

$320 - 960y + 160y = 120$

$\qquad 320 - 800y = 120$

$\qquad -800y = -200$

$\qquad y = \dfrac{-200}{-800}$

$\qquad y = \dfrac{1}{4} = 0.25$

Substitute the value for $y$ into one of the equations and solve for $x$.
$$x + 240y = 80$$
$$x + 240(0.25) = 80$$
$$x + 60 = 80$$
$$x = 20$$
So, the solution of the system is (20, 0.25).
20 represents the cost per day: $20. 0.25 represents the cost per mile: $0.25.

## Guided Practice

1. Solve an equation for one variable.
$$y = 2x - 7$$
Substitute the expression for $y$ in the other equation and solve.
$$3x - 2y = 9$$
$$3x - 2(2x - 7) = 9$$
$$3x - 4x + 14 = 9$$
$$-x + 14 = 9$$
$$-x = -5$$
$$x = 5$$
Substitute the value for $x$ into one of the equations and solve for $y$.
$$y = 2x - 7$$
$$y = 2(5) - 7$$
$$y = 10 - 7 = 3$$
The solution is (5, 3).

2. Solve an equation for one variable.
$$y = x - 4$$
Substitute the expression for $y$ in the other equation and solve.
$$2x + y = 5$$
$$2x + (x - 4) = 5$$
$$3x - 4 = 5$$
$$3x = 9$$
$$x = 3$$
Substitute the value for $x$ into one of the equations and solve for $y$.
$$y = x - 4$$
$$y = 3 - 4$$
$$y = -1$$
The solution is (3, −1).

3. Solve an equation for one variable.
$$y = -x + 3$$
Substitute the expression for $y$ in the other equationand solve.
$$x + 4y = 6$$
$$x + 4(-x + 3) = 6$$
$$x - 4x + 12 = 6$$
$$-3x + 12 = 6$$
$$-3x = -6$$
$$x = 2$$
Substitute the value for $x$ into one of the equations and solve for $y$.
$$y = -x + 3$$
$$y = -(2) + 3$$
$$y = 1$$
The solution is (2, 1).

4. Solve an equation for one variable.
$$x - y = 3$$
$$x = 3 + y$$
Substitute the expression for $x$ in the other equation and solve.
$$x + 2y = 6$$
$$3 + y + 2y = 6$$
$$3 + 3y = 6$$
$$3y = 3$$
$$y = 1$$
Substitute the value for $y$ into one of the equations and solve for $x$.
$$x - y = 3$$
$$x - 1 = 3$$
$$x = 4$$
The solution is (4, 1).

5. Sketch the graph of each equation.

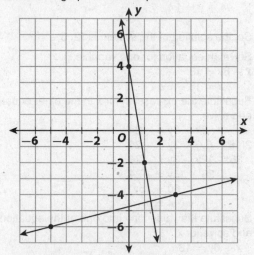

Find the intersection of the lines.
The lines appear to intersect near (1, −4).
The estimated solution is (1, −4).
Solve the system of equations.
Solve an equation for one variable.
$$6x + y = 4$$
$$y = 4 - 6x$$
Substitute the expression for $y$ in the other equation and solve.
$$x - 4y = 19$$
$$x - 4(4 - 6x) = 19$$
$$x - 16 + 24x = 19$$
$$25x - 16 = 19$$
$$25x = 35$$
$$x = \frac{35}{25} = \frac{7}{5}$$
Substitute the value for $x$ into one of the equations and solve for $y$.
$$x - 4y = 19$$
$$\frac{7}{5} - 4y = 19$$
$$-4y = 19 - \frac{7}{5} = \frac{88}{5}$$
$$y = -\frac{22}{5}$$
The solution is $\left(\frac{7}{5}, -\frac{22}{5}\right)$.

6. Sketch the graph of each equation.

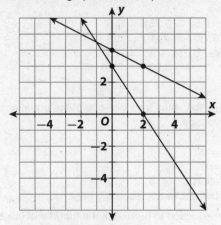

The lines appear to intersect near $(-1, 5)$.
The estimated solution is $(-1, 5)$.
Solve the system of equations.
Solve an equation for one variable.
$x + 2y = 8$
$\quad x = 8 - 2y$
Substitute the expression for $x$ in the other equation and solve.
$3x + 2y = 6$
$3(8 - 2y) + 2y = 6$
$24 - 6y + 2y = 6$
$24 - 4y = 6$
$-4y = -18$
$y = \dfrac{18}{4} = \dfrac{9}{2}$
Substitute the value for $y$ into one of the equations and solve for $x$.
$x + 2y = 8$
$x + 2\left(\dfrac{9}{2}\right) = 8$
$x + 9 = 8$
$x = -1$
The solution is $\left(-1, \dfrac{9}{2}\right)$.

7. Sketch the graph of each equation.

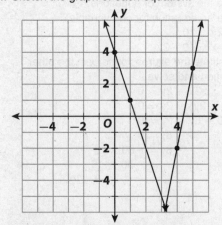

The lines appear to intersect near $(3, -6)$.
The estimated solution is $(3, -6)$.
Solve the system of equations.
Solve an equation for one variable.
$3x + y = 4$
$\quad y = 4 - 3x$

Substitute the expression for $y$ in the other equation and solve.
$5x - y = 22$
$5x - (4 - 3x) = 22$
$5x - 4 + 3x = 22$
$8x - 4 = 22$
$8x = 26$
$x = \dfrac{26}{8} = \dfrac{13}{4}$
Substitute the value for $x$ into one of the equations and solve for $y$.
$3x + y = 4$
$3\left(\dfrac{13}{4}\right) + y = 4$
$\dfrac{39}{4} + y = 4$
$y = 4 - \dfrac{39}{4} = -\dfrac{23}{4}$
The solution is $\left(\dfrac{13}{4}, -\dfrac{23}{4}\right)$.

8. Sketch the graph of each equation.

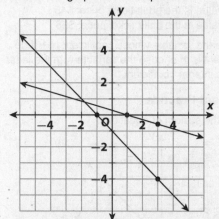

The lines appear to intersect near $(-2, 1)$.
The estimated solution is $(-2, 1)$.
Solve the system of equations.
Solve an equation for one variable.
$x + y = -1$
$\quad y = -x - 1$
Substitute the expression for $y$ in the other equation and solve.
$2x + 7(-x - 1) = 2$
$2x - 7x - 7 = 2$
$-5x - 7 = 2$
$-5x = 9$
$x = -\dfrac{9}{5}$
Substitute the value for $x$ into one of the equations and solve for $y$.
$x + y = -1$
$-\dfrac{9}{5} + y = -1$
$y = -1 + \dfrac{9}{5} = \dfrac{4}{5}$
The solution is $\left(-\dfrac{9}{5}, \dfrac{4}{5}\right)$.

9. a. Hensons' cost: $3x + y = 163$
      Garcias' cost: $2x + 3y = 174$
   b. Solve the system of equations.
      Solve an equation for one variable.
      $3x + y = 163$
      $\quad y = -3x + 163$
      Substitute the expression for $y$ in the other equation and solve.
      $2x + 3(-3x + 163) = 174$
      $\quad 2x - 9x + 489 = 174$
      $\quad\quad\quad -7x = 174 - 489$
      $\quad\quad\quad -7x = -315$
      $\quad\quad\quad\quad x = 45$
      Substitute the value for $x$ into one of the equations and solve for $y$.
      $\quad 3x + y = 163$
      $3(45) + y = 163$
      $\quad 135 + y = 163$
      $\quad\quad\quad y = 28$
      The solution is $(45, 28)$.
      The $x$ value is the adult ticket price: $45
      The $y$ value is the child ticket price: $28

10. Choose the variable whose coefficient is 1. If no coefficient is 1, choose the variable with the least positive integer coefficient.

## Independent Practice

11. Graph the system of equations.

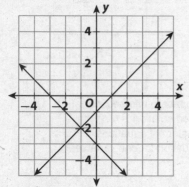

The graph shows that the $x$-coordinate of the solution is negative, so Zach's solution is not reasonable.

12. a. Write an equation to represent the number of pieces of fruit.
      Let $x =$ the number of apples. Let $y =$ the number of bananas.
      $x + y = 20$
      Write an equation to represent the money spent on the fruit.
      $0.50x + 0.75y = 11.50$
   b. Solve the system of equations.
      Solve an equation for one variable.
      $x + y = 20$
      $\quad y = -x + 20$

Substitute the expression for $y$ in the other equation and solve.
$\quad\quad 0.5x + 0.75y = 11.5$
$0.5x + 0.75(-x + 20) = 11.5$
$\quad 0.5x - 0.75x + 15 = 11.5$
$\quad\quad\quad\quad -0.25x = -3.5$
$\quad\quad\quad\quad\quad x = \dfrac{-3.5}{-0.25} = 14$
Substitute the value for $x$ into one of the equations and solve for $y$.
$\quad x + y = 20$
$14 + y = 20$
$\quad\quad y = 6$
The solution is $(14, 6)$.
Angelo bought 14 apples and 6 bananas.

13. Write an equation to represent the number of coins.
    Let $n =$ the number of nickels. Let $d =$ the number of dimes.
    $n + d = 200$
    Write an equation to represent the value of the coins.
    $0.05n + 0.1d = 14$
    Solve the system of equations.
    Solve an equation for one variable.
    $\quad n + d = 200$
    $\quad n = 200 - d$
    Substitute the expression for $n$ in the other equation and solve.
    $\quad\quad\quad 0.05n + 0.1d = 14$
    $0.05(200 - d) + 0.1d = 14$
    $\quad 10 - 0.05d + 0.1d = 14$
    $\quad\quad\quad 10 + 0.05d = 14$
    $\quad\quad\quad\quad 0.05d = 4$
    $\quad\quad\quad\quad\quad d = 80$
    Substitute the value for $d$ into one of the equations and solve for $n$.
    $\quad n + d = 200$
    $n + 80 = 200$
    $\quad\quad n = 120$
    There are 120 nickels and 80 dimes in the jar.

14. a. Solve the system of equations.
       Solve an equation for one variable.
       $x + 2y = 10$
       $\quad x = 10 - 2y$
       Substitute the expression for $x$ in the other equation and solve.
       $\quad\quad 3x - 2y = 0$
       $3(10 - 2y) - 2y = 0$
       $\quad 30 - 6y - 2y = 0$
       $\quad\quad 30 - 8y = 0$
       $\quad\quad\quad -8y = -30$
       $\quad\quad\quad\quad y = \dfrac{-30}{-8} = \dfrac{15}{4}$

Substitute the value for $y$ into one of the equations and solve for $x$.

$$x + 2y = 10$$
$$x + 2\left(\frac{15}{4}\right) = 10$$
$$x + \frac{30}{4} = 10$$
$$x = 10 - \frac{30}{4}$$
$$x = \frac{10}{4} = \frac{5}{2}$$

The solution is $\left(\frac{5}{2}, \frac{15}{4}\right)$.

Point $A$: $\left(\frac{5}{2}, \frac{15}{4}\right)$

b. The height of the triangle is the $y$-coordinate of Point $A$.

Height: $\frac{15}{4}$ units

c. The base of the triangle is the distance between the $x$-coordinates of the two lines as they cross the $x$-axis. The lines cross at $(0, 0)$ and $(10, 0)$.

$$10 - 0 = 10$$

Base: 10 units

d. Find the area of the triangle.

$$A = \frac{1}{2}bh$$
$$= \frac{1}{2}(10)\left(\frac{15}{4}\right)$$
$$= \frac{75}{4} = 18\frac{3}{4}$$

The area of the triangle is $18\frac{3}{4}$ square units.

15. Write the equations of the lines for the struts. Find the slope of the line through points $A$ and $C$.

$$m = \frac{\frac{2}{3} - \left(-\frac{16}{3}\right)}{\frac{4}{3} - \frac{14}{3}}$$
$$= \frac{\frac{18}{3}}{-\frac{18}{3}} = -1$$

Find the slope of the line through points $B$ and $D$.

$$m = \frac{-\frac{4}{3} - \left(-\frac{16}{3}\right)}{\frac{14}{3} - \frac{2}{3}}$$
$$= \frac{\frac{12}{3}}{\frac{12}{3}} = 1$$

Write equations in slope-intercept form.
Find the equation for the line through points $A$ and $C$.

$$y = mx + b$$
$$\frac{2}{3} = -\left(-\frac{4}{3}\right) + b$$
$$\frac{2}{3} = \frac{4}{3} + b$$
$$-\frac{2}{3} = b$$
$$y = -x - \frac{2}{3}$$

Find the equation for the line through points $B$ and $D$.

$$y = mx + b$$
$$-\frac{4}{3} = \left(\frac{14}{3}\right) + b$$
$$-\frac{18}{3} = b$$
$$-6 = b$$
$$y = x - 6$$

Solve the system of equations to find the intersection of the two lines.
Solve an equation for one variable.

$$y = x - 6$$

Substitute the expression for $y$ in the other equation and solve.

$$y = -x - \frac{2}{3}$$
$$x - 6 = -x - \frac{2}{3}$$
$$2x = 6 - \frac{2}{3}$$
$$2x = \frac{16}{3}$$
$$x = \frac{8}{3}$$

Substitute the value for $x$ into one of the equations and solve for $y$.

$$y = x - 6$$
$$y = \frac{8}{3} - 6$$
$$y = \frac{8}{3} - \frac{18}{3} = -\frac{10}{3}$$

The struts cross at the point $\left(\frac{8}{3}, -\frac{10}{3}\right)$.

## Focus on Higher Order Thinking

16. Solve the second equation for $x$ ($x = -8 - 3y$) and then substitute that value into the first equation. Solve the first equation for $y$ ($y = 2x - 5$) and then substitute that value into the second equation. Solve either equation for $3y$ ($3y = -8 - x$ or $3y = 6x - 15$) and then substitute that value into the other equation. Solve an equation for one variable.

$$x + 3y = -8$$
$$x = -8 - 3y$$

Substitute the expression for $x$ in the other equation and solve.

$$6x - 3y = 15$$
$$6(-8 - 3y) - 3y = 15$$
$$-48 - 18y - 3y = 15$$
$$-48 - 21y = 15$$
$$-21y = 63$$
$$y = -3$$

Substitute the value for $y$ into one of the equations and solve for $x$.

$$x + 3y = -8$$
$$x + 3(-3) = -8$$
$$x - 9 = -8$$
$$x = 1$$

Solution: $(1, -3)$

17. The substitution method has the advantage of always giving an exact answer. Using graphing produces an exact answer only if the solution is an ordered pair whose coordinates are integers.

18. Let $A = 1$, $B = 3$, $D = -2$, $E = -4$.

Substitute $x = 7$ and $y = -2$ into the equations and solve for $C$ and $F$.

$$x + 3y = C$$
$$7 + 3(-2) = C$$
$$1 = C$$
$$-2x - 4y = F$$
$$-2(7) - 4(-2) = F$$
$$-14 + 8 = F$$
$$-6 = F$$

Sample answer: $\begin{cases} x + 3y = 1 \\ -2x - 4y = -6 \end{cases}$, I chose random

values of $A$, $B$, $D$, and $E$, substituted them into the equations, and calculated the values of $C$ and $F$ using $x = 7$ and $y = -2$.

## LESSON 8.3

### Your Turn

3. Add the equations.

$$\begin{array}{r} x + y = -1 \\ + x - y = 7 \\ \hline 2x = 6 \\ x = 3 \end{array}$$

Substitute the value for $x$ into one of the equations.

$$x + y = -1$$
$$3 + y = -1$$
$$y = -4$$

The solution is $(3, -4)$.

Graphing the two equations checks the solution.

4. Add the equations.

$$\begin{array}{r} 2x + 2y = -2 \\ + 3x - 2y = 12 \\ \hline 5x = 10 \\ x = 2 \end{array}$$

Substitute the value for $x$ into one of the equations.

$$2x + 2y = -2$$
$$2(2) + 2y = -2$$
$$4 + 2y = -2$$
$$2y = -6$$
$$y = -3$$

The solution is $(2, -3)$.

Graphing the two equations checks the solution.

5. Add the equations.

$$\begin{array}{r} 6x + 5y = 4 \\ + (-6x + 7y = 20) \\ \hline 12y = 24 \\ y = 2 \end{array}$$

Substitute the value for $y$ into one of the equations.

$$6x + 5y = 4$$
$$6x + 5(2) = 4$$
$$6x + 10 = 4$$
$$6x = -6$$
$$x = -1$$

The solution is $(-1, 2)$.

Graphing the two equations checks the solution.

8. Subtract the equations.

$$\begin{array}{r} 6x - 3y = 6 \\ -(6x + 8y = -16) \\ \hline -11y = 22 \\ y = -2 \end{array}$$

Substitute the value for $y$ into one of the equations.

$$6x - 3y = 6$$
$$6x - 3(-2) = 6$$
$$6x + 6 = 6$$
$$x = 0$$

The solution is $(0, -2)$.

Graphing the two equations checks the solution.

9. Subtract the equations.

$$\begin{array}{r} 4x + 3y = 19 \\ -(6x + 3y = 33) \\ \hline -2x = -14 \\ x = 7 \end{array}$$

Substitute the value for $x$ into one of the equations.

$$4x + 3y = 19$$
$$4(7) + 3y = 19$$
$$28 + 3y = 19$$
$$3y = -9$$
$$y = -3$$

The solution is $(7, -3)$.

Graphing the two equations checks the solution.

10. Subtract the equations.

$$\begin{array}{r} 2x + 6y = 17 \\ -(2x - 10y = 9) \\ \hline 16y = 8 \\ y = \frac{1}{2} \end{array}$$

Substitute the value for $y$ into one of the equations.

$$2x + 6y = 17$$
$$2x + 6\left(\frac{1}{2}\right) = 17$$
$$2x + 3 = 17$$
$$2x = 14$$
$$x = 7$$

The solution is $\left(7, \frac{1}{2}\right)$.

Graphing the two equations checks the solution.

11. Choose variables and write a system of equations.

Let $x$ represent the length of a guppy, in inches.

Let $y$ represent the length of a platy, in inches.

Marta's aquarium: $3x + 2y = 13$

Hank's aquarium: $3x + 4y = 17$

Subtract the equations.

$$\begin{array}{r} 3x + 4y = 17 \\ -(3x + 2y = 13) \\ \hline 2y = 4 \\ y = 2 \end{array}$$

Substitute the value of $y$ into one of the equations.

$$3x + 2y = 13$$
$$3x + 2(2) = 13$$
$$3x + 4 = 13$$
$$3x = 9$$
$$x = 3$$

The guppies are 3 inches long and the platies are 2 inches long.

## Guided Practice

1. Add the equations.
$$4x + 3y = 1$$
$$\underline{+ \; x - 3y = -11}$$
$$5x + 0 = -10$$
Add to eliminate the variable $y$.
$$5x = -10$$
Divide both sides by 5 and simplify.
$$x = -2$$
Substitute the value for $x$ into one of the equations.
$$x - 3y = -11$$
$$(-2) - 3y = -11$$
$$-3y = -9$$
$$y = 3$$
So, $(-2, 3)$ is the solution of the system.

2. Subtract the equations.
$$x + 2y = -2$$
$$\underline{-(-3x + 2y = -10)}$$
$$4x + 0 = 8$$
$$x = 2$$
Substitute the value for $x$ into one of the equations.
$$x + 2y = -2$$
$$2 + 2y = -2$$
$$2y = -4$$
$$y = -2$$
The solution is $(2, -2)$.

3. Subtract the equations.
$$3x + y = 23$$
$$\underline{-(3x - 2y = 8)}$$
$$0 + 3y = 15$$
$$y = 5$$
Substitute the value for $y$ into one of the equations.
$$3x + y = 23$$
$$3x + 5 = 23$$
$$3x = 18$$
$$x = 6$$
The solution is $(6, 5)$.

4. Add the equations.
$$-4x - 5y = 7$$
$$\underline{+ \; 3x + 5y = -14}$$
$$-x + 0 = -7$$
$$-x = -7$$
$$x = 7$$
Substitute the value for $x$ into one of the equations.
$$3x + 5y = -14$$
$$3(7) + 5y = -14$$
$$21 + 5y = -14$$
$$5y = -35$$
$$y = -7$$
The solution is $(7, -7)$.

5. Add the equations.
$$x - 2y = -19$$
$$\underline{+ \; 5x + 2y = 1}$$
$$6x + 0 = -18$$
$$6x = -18$$
$$x = -3$$

Substitute the value for $x$ into one of the equations.
$$x - 2y = -19$$
$$(-3) - 2y = -19$$
$$-2y = -16$$
$$y = 8$$
The solution is $(-3, 8)$.

6. Subtract the equations.
$$3x + 4y = 18$$
$$\underline{-(-2x + 4y = 8)}$$
$$5x + 0 = 10$$
$$5x = 10$$
$$x = 2$$
Substitute the value for $x$ into one of the equations.
$$3x + 4y = 18$$
$$3(2) + 4y = 18$$
$$6 + 4y = 18$$
$$4y = 12$$
$$y = 3$$
The solution is $(2, 3)$.

7. Subtract the equations.
$$-5x + 7y = 11$$
$$\underline{-(-5x + 3y = 19)}$$
$$0 + 4y = -8$$
$$4y = -8$$
$$y = -2$$
Substitute the value for $y$ into one of the equations.
$$-5x + 7y = 11$$
$$-5x + 7(-2) = 11$$
$$-5x - 14 = 11$$
$$-5x = 25$$
$$x = -5$$
The solution is $(-5, -2)$.

8. Write equations to represent Tony's distance and Rae's distance.
Let $x$ represent the minimum speed limit.
Let $y$ represent the maximum speed limit.
Tony: $2x + 3.5y = 355$
Rae: $2x + 3y = 320$
Solve the system.
Subtract the equations.
$$2x + 3.5y = 355$$
$$\underline{-(2x + 3y = 320)}$$
$$0 + 0.5y = 35$$
$$y = 70$$
Substitute the value for $y$ into one of the equations.
$$2x + 3y = 320$$
$$2x + 3(70) = 320$$
$$2x + 210 = 320$$
$$2x = 110$$
$$x = 55$$
Minimum speed limit: 55 mi/h
Maximum speed limit: 70 mi/h

9. No; addition or subtraction can be used only when the coefficients of the $x$-terms or the $y$-terms are the same or opposites.

## Independent Practice

10. Write equations to represent Marta's purchase and Hank's purchase.

    Let $x$ represent the price of a guppy.
    Let $y$ represent the price of a platy.
    Marta: $3x + 2y = 13.95$
    Hank: $3x + 4y = 18.33$
    Solve the system.
    Subtract the equations.

    $$3x + 2y = 13.95$$
    $$\underline{-(3x + 4y = 18.33)}$$
    $$0 - 2y = -4.38$$
    $$y = 2.19$$

    Substitute the value for $y$ into one of the equations.

    $$3x + 2y = 13.95$$
    $$3x + 2(2.19) = 13.95$$
    $$3x + 4.38 = 13.95$$
    $$3x = 9.57$$
    $$x = 3.19$$

    The price of a guppy: $3.19
    The price of a platy: $2.19

11. Write equations to represent Marta's aquarium and Hank's aquarium.

    Let $x$ represent the length of a guppy.
    Let $y$ represent the length of a platy.
    Marta: $3x + 2y = 13$
    Hank: $3x + 4y = 17$
    Solve the system.
    Subtract the equations.

    $$3x + 2y = 13$$
    $$\underline{-(3x + 4y = 17)}$$
    $$0 - 2y = -4$$
    $$-2y = -4$$
    $$y = 2$$

    Substitute the value for $y$ into one of the equations.

    $$3x + 2y = 13$$
    $$3x + 2(2) = 13$$
    $$3x + 4 = 13$$
    $$3x = 9$$
    $$x = 3$$

    The length of a guppy: 3 in.
    The length of a platy: 2 in.

12. Find the slope of line $m$ through points $(6, 1)$ and $(2, -3)$.

    $$\text{Slope of line } m = \frac{1 - (-3)}{6 - 2}$$
    $$= \frac{4}{4} = 1$$

    Find the slope of line $n$ through points $(2, 3)$ and $(5, -6)$.

    $$\text{Slope of line } n = \frac{-6 - 3}{5 - 2}$$
    $$= \frac{-9}{3} = -3$$

    Write equations in slope-intercept form.
    Find the equation for the line $m$.

    $$y = mx + b$$
    $$1 = 1(6) + b$$
    $$1 = 6 + b$$
    $$-5 = b$$
    $$y = x - 5$$

Find the equation for line $n$.

$$y = mx + b$$
$$3 = -3(2) + b$$
$$3 = -6 + b$$
$$9 = b$$
$$y = -3x + 9$$

Solve the system of equations to find the intersection of the two lines.
Subtract the equations.

$$y = x - 5$$
$$\underline{-(y = -3x + 9)}$$
$$0 = 4x - 14$$
$$14 = 4x$$
$$\frac{14}{4} = x$$
$$x = \frac{7}{2}$$

Substitute the value for $x$ into one of the equations.

$$y = x - 5$$
$$y = \frac{7}{2} - 5$$
$$y = \frac{7 - 10}{2}$$
$$y = -\frac{3}{2}$$

The intersection of the two lines is $\left(\frac{7}{2}, -\frac{3}{2}\right)$.

13. Write equations to represent the 5-quart oil change and the 7-quart oil change.

    Let $x$ represent the cost of 1 quart of oil.
    Let $y$ represent the labor fee.
    5-qt oil change: $5x + y = 22.45$
    7-qt oil change: $7x + y = 25.45$
    Solve the system.
    Subtract the equations.

    $$5x + y = 22.45$$
    $$\underline{-(7x + y = 25.45)}$$
    $$-2x + 0 = -3.00$$
    $$-2x = -3.00$$
    $$x = 1.50$$

    Substitute the value for $x$ into one of the equations.

    $$5x + y = 22.45$$
    $$5(1.5) + y = 22.45$$
    $$7.5 + y = 22.45$$
    $$y = 14.95$$

    The cost of 1 quart of oil: $1.50
    The labor fee: $14.95

14. Find the selling price of style B in July.
    22% discount means the selling price is
    $100 - 22 = 78\%$ of the original price.
    $0.78 \times \$22.95 = \$17.90$
    The selling price of style B in July was $17.90.
    Write the equations for the T-shirts sold in June and July.
    Let $x$ represent the number of style A T-shirts.
    Let $y$ represent the number of style B T-shirts.
    June: $x(15.95) + y(22.95) = 2779$
    July: $x(15.95) + y(17.90) = 2385.10$
    Solve the system.

Subtract the equations.

$x(15.95) + y(22.95) = 2779$
$-[x(15.95) + y(17.90) = 2385.10]$
$0 + y(5.05) = 393.9$
$y(5.05) = 393.9$
$y = 78$

Substitute the value for $y$ into one of the equations.

$x(15.95) + y(22.95) = 2779$
$x(15.95) + (78)(22.95) = 2779$
$x(15.95) + 1790.1 = 2779$
$x(15.95) = 988.9$
$x = 62$

Find the number of shirts sold each month:
$62 + 78 = 140$
Total for the two months: $2 \times 140 = 280$
280 T-shirts of style A and style B were sold in June and July.

15. Write the equations for the total tickets sold to the basketball game and for the amount collected on the sale of the tickets.
Let $x$ represent the number of adult tickets sold.
Let $y$ represent the number of student tickets sold.
Total ticket sales: $x + y = 1{,}246$
Amount collected from ticket sales: $5x + y = 2{,}874$
Solve the system.
Subtract the equations.

$5x + y = 2{,}874$
$-(x + y = 1{,}246)$
$4x + 0 = 1{,}628$
$4x = 1{,}628$
$x = 407$

Substitute the value for $x$ into one of the equations.

$x + y = 1{,}246$
$407 + y = 1{,}246$
$y = 839$

407 adult tickets and 839 student tickets were sold.

### Focus on Higher Order Thinking

16. Yes; solve the second equation for $x$ to get $x = -2y + 6$.
Substitute $-2y + 6$ for $x$ in the first equation to get $3(-2y + 6) - 2y = 10$. Solve this for $y$ to get $y = 1$.
Then substitute 1 for $y$ in either original equation to get $x = 4$, for a solution of $(4, 1)$. The elimination method is more efficient because there are fewer calculations and they are simpler to do.

17. a. She substituted her expression for $y$ in the same equation she used to find $y$. She should substitute her expression into the other equation.
    b. Yes; adding the equations would have resulted in $3x = 9$, easily giving $x = 3$ after dividing each side by 3. Substitution requires many more steps.

## LESSON 8.4

### Your Turn

4. Multiply one of the equations by a constant.
$-3(5x + 2y = -10)$
$-15x - 6y = 30$
Add the equations.
$-15x - 6y = 30$
$+\ \ 3x + 6y = 66$
$-12x + 0 = 96$
$-12x = 96$
$\dfrac{-12x}{-12} = \dfrac{96}{-12}$
$x = -8$
Substitute the value for $x$ into one of the equations.
$3x + 6y = 66$
$3(-8) + 6y = 66$
$-24 + 6y = 66$
$6y = 90$
$y = 15$
The solution is $(-8, 15)$.

5. Multiply one of the equations by a constant.
$3x - y = -8$
$2(3x - y = -8)$
$6x - 2y = -16$
Add the equations.
$6x - 2y = -16$
$+4x + 2y = 6$
$10x + 0 = -10$
$10x = -10$
$x = -1$
Substitute the value for $x$ into one of the equations.
$4x + 2y = 6$
$4(-1) + 2y = 6$
$-4 + 2y = 6$
$2y = 10$
$y = 5$
The solution is $(-1, 5)$.

6. Multiply one of the equations by a constant.
$2x + y = 0$
$3(2x + y = 0)$
$6x + 3y = 0$
Add the equations.
$-6x + 9y = -12$
$+\ 6x + 3y = 0$
$0 + 12y = -12$
$12y = -12$
$y = -1$
Substitute the value for $x$ into one of the equations.
$2x + y = 0$
$2x + (-1) = 0$
$2x = 1$
$x = \dfrac{1}{2}$

The solution is $\left(\dfrac{1}{2}, -1\right)$.

7. Multiply one of the equations by a constant.

$$3x - 7y = 2$$
$$2(3x - 7y = 2)$$
$$6x - 14y = 4$$

Subtract the equations.

$$6x - 14y = 4$$
$$\underline{-(6x - 9y = 9)}$$
$$0 - 5y = -5$$
$$y = 1$$

Substitute the value for $x$ into one of the equations.

$$3x - 7y = 2$$
$$3x - 7(1) = 2$$
$$3x - 7 = 2$$
$$3x = 9$$
$$x = 3$$

The solution is $(3, 1)$.

8. Multiply one of the equations by a constant.

$$-3x + y = 11$$
$$3(-3x + y = 11)$$
$$-9x + 3y = 33$$

Subtract the equations.

$$-9x + 3y = 33$$
$$\underline{-(2x + 3y = -11)}$$
$$-11x + 0 = 44$$
$$-11x = 44$$
$$x = -4$$

Substitute the value for $x$ into one of the equations.

$$2x + 3y = -11$$
$$2(-4) + 3y = -11$$
$$-8 + 3y = -11$$
$$3y = -3$$
$$y = -1$$

The solution is $(-4, -1)$.

9. Multiply one of the equations by a constant.

$$3x - 2y = -11$$
$$3(3x - 2y = -11)$$
$$9x - 6y = -33$$

Subtract the equations.

$$9x + y = 9$$
$$\underline{-(9x - 6y = -33)}$$
$$0 + 7y = 42$$
$$7y = 42$$
$$y = 6$$

Substitute the value for $y$ into one of the equations.

$$9x + y = 9$$
$$9x + (6) = 9$$
$$9x = 3$$
$$x = \frac{3}{9} = \frac{1}{3}$$

The solution is $\left(\frac{1}{3}, 6\right)$.

10. Choose variables and write a system of equations.

Let $x$ represent the length of time running.
Let $y$ represent the length of time biking.
Jason: $5.2x + 20.6y = 14.2$
Seth: $10.4x + 18.4y = 17$

Multiply both equations by 10 to eliminate the decimals.

$$10(5.2x + 20.6y = 14.2) \rightarrow 52x + 206y = 142$$
$$10(10.4x + 18.4y = 17) \rightarrow 104x + 184y = 170$$

Multiply one of the equations by a constant.

$$52x + 206y = 142$$
$$2(52x + 206y = 142)$$
$$104x + 412y = 284$$

Subtract the equations.

$$104x + 412y = 284$$
$$\underline{-(104x + 184y = 170)}$$
$$0 + 228y = 114$$
$$228y = 114$$
$$\frac{228y}{228} = \frac{114}{228}$$
$$y = \frac{1}{2} = 0.5$$

Substitute the value for $y$ into one of the equations.

$$52x + 206y = 142$$
$$52x + 206\left(\frac{1}{2}\right) = 142$$
$$52x + 103 = 142$$
$$52x = 39$$
$$\frac{52x}{52} = \frac{39}{52}$$
$$x = \frac{3}{4} = 0.75$$

Contestants run 0.75 hour and bike 0.5 hour.

## Guided Practice

1. Multiply the first equation by 4. Add to the second equation.

$$4(3x - y = 8)$$
$$12x - 4y = 32$$
$$\underline{+(-2x) + 4y = -12}$$

Add to eliminate the variable $y$.

$$10x = 20$$

Divide both sides by 10 and simplify.

$$x = 2$$

Substitute the value for $x$ into one of the original equations and solve for $y$.

$$3x - y = 8$$
$$3(2) - y = 8$$
$$6 - y = 8$$
$$-y = 2$$
$$y = -2$$

So, $(2, -2)$ is the solution of the system.

2. Multiply one of the equations by a constant.

$$x + 4y = 2$$
$$2(x + 4y = 2)$$
$$2x + 8y = 4$$

Subtract the equations.

$$2x + 8y = 4$$
$$-(2x + 5y = 7)$$
$$\phantom{2x + {}}3y = -3$$
$$\phantom{2x + {}}y = -1$$

Substitute the value for $y$ into one of the equations.

$$x + 4y = 2$$
$$x + 4(-1) = 2$$
$$x + -4 = 2$$
$$x = 6$$

The solution is $(6, -1)$.

3. Multiply one of the equations by a constant.

$$3x + y = -1$$
$$3(3x + y = -1)$$
$$9x + 3y = -3$$

Subtract the equations.

$$9x + 3y = -3$$
$$-(2x + 3y = 18)$$
$$7x + 0 = -21$$
$$7x = -21$$
$$x = -3$$

Substitute the value for $x$ into one of the equations.

$$3x + y = -1$$
$$3(-3) + y = -1$$
$$-9 + y = -1$$
$$y = 8$$

The solution is $(-3, 8)$.

4. Multiply one of the equations by a constant.

$$6x - 4y = 14$$
$$2(6x - 4y = 14)$$
$$12x - 8y = 28$$

Add the equations.

$$2x + 8y = 21$$
$$+12x - 8y = 28$$
$$14x + 0 = 49$$
$$14x = 49$$
$$\frac{14x}{14} = \frac{49}{14}$$
$$x = \frac{7}{2}$$

Substitute the value for $x$ into one of the equations.

$$2x + 8y = 21$$
$$2\left(\frac{7}{2}\right) + 8y = 21$$
$$7 + 8y = 21$$
$$8y = 14$$
$$y = \frac{14}{8} = \frac{7}{4}$$

The solution is $\left(\frac{7}{2}, \frac{7}{4}\right)$.

5. Multiply one of the equations by a constant.

$$-x + 3y = -12$$
$$2(-x + 3y = -12)$$
$$-2x + 6y = -24$$

Add the equations.

$$2x + y = 3$$
$$+(-2x + 6y = -24)$$
$$0 + 7y = -21$$
$$7y = -21$$
$$y = -3$$

Substitute the value for $y$ into one of the equations.

$$2x + y = 3$$
$$2x + (-3) = 3$$
$$2x = 6$$
$$x = 3$$

The solution is $(3, -3)$.

6. Multiply one of the equations by a constant.

$$2x + 3y = 5$$
$$3(2x + 3y = 5)$$
$$6x + 9y = 15$$

Subtract the equations.

$$6x + 5y = 19$$
$$-(6x + 9y = 15)$$
$$0 - 4y = 4$$
$$-4y = 4$$
$$y = -1$$

Substitute the value for $y$ into one of the equations.

$$2x + 3y = 5$$
$$2x + 3(-1) = 5$$
$$2x - 3 = 5$$
$$2x = 8$$
$$x = 4$$

The solution is $(4, -1)$.

7. Multiply one of the equations by a constant.

$$2x + 5y = 16$$
$$2(2x + 5y = 16)$$
$$4x + 10y = 32$$

Add the equations.

$$4x + 10y = 32$$
$$+(-4x + 3y = 20)$$
$$0 + 13y = 52$$
$$13y = 52$$
$$y = 4$$

Substitute the value for $y$ into one of the equations.

$$2x + 5y = 16$$
$$2x + 5(4) = 16$$
$$2x + 20 = 16$$
$$2x = -4$$
$$x = -2$$

The solution is $(-2, 4)$.

8. a. Write equations to represent Bryce's expenditures at each store.
   Let $x$ represent the number apples.
   Let $y$ represent the number of pears.
   First store: $0.64x + 0.45y = 5.26$
   Second store: $0.32x + 0.39y = 3.62$

   b. Solve the system.
   Multiply both equations by 100 to eliminate the decimals.
   $100(0.64x + 0.45y = 5.26) \rightarrow 64x + 45y = 526$
   $100(0.32x + 0.39y = 3.62) \rightarrow 32x + 39y = 362$
   Multiply one of the equations by a constant.
   $$32x + 39y = 362$$
   $$2(32x + 39y = 362)$$
   $$64x + 78y = 724$$
   Subtract the equations.
   $$64x + 78y = 724$$
   $$\underline{-(64x + 45y = 526)}$$
   $$0 + 33y = 198$$
   $$33y = 198$$
   $$y = 6$$
   Substitute the value for $y$ into one of the equations.
   $$32x + 39y = 362$$
   $$32x + 39(6) = 362$$
   $$32x + 234 = 362$$
   $$32x = 128$$
   $$\frac{32x}{32} = \frac{128}{32}$$
   $$x = 4$$
   Number of apples: 4
   Number of pears: 6

9. If the coefficients of one variable are the same, you subtract. If the coefficients of one variable are opposites, you add.

## Independent Practice

10. Gwen forgot to multiply the right side by 2.
    Multiply one of the equations by a constant.
    $$x - 3y = -1$$
    $$2(x - 3y = -1)$$
    $$2x - 6y = -2$$
    Add the equations.
    $$2x + 6y = 3$$
    $$\underline{+2x - 6y = -2}$$
    $$4x + 0 = 1$$
    $$4x = 1$$
    $$x = \frac{1}{4}$$
    Substitute the value for $x$ into one of the equations.
    $$x - 3y = -1$$
    $$\left(\frac{1}{4}\right) - 3y = -1$$
    $$-3y = -\frac{5}{4}$$
    $$\frac{-3y}{-3} = -\frac{5}{4(-3)}$$
    $$y = \frac{5}{12}$$
    The solution is $\left(\frac{1}{4}, \frac{5}{12}\right)$.

11. a. Let $x$ represent the number of polyester-fill sleeping bags.
    Let $y$ represent the number of down-fill sleeping bags.
    Cost of bags sold: $79x + 149y = 1,456$
    Total bags sold: $x + y = 14$

    b. Multiply the second equation by 79. Subtract the new equation from the first one and solve the resulting equation for $y$.

    c. Solve the second equation for $x$. Substitute the expression for $x$ in the first equation and solve the resulting equation for $y$.

    d. Multiply one of the equations by a constant.
    $$x + y = 14$$
    $$79(x + y = 14)$$
    $$79x + 79y = 1,106$$
    Subtract the equations.
    $$79x + 149y = 1,456$$
    $$\underline{-(79x + 79y = 1,106)}$$
    $$0 + 70y = 1,350$$
    $$70y = 350$$
    $$y = 5$$
    Substitute the value for $y$ into one of the equations.
    $$x + y = 14$$
    $$x + 5 = 14$$
    $$x = 9$$
    9 polyester-fill sleeping bags and 5 down-fill sleeping bags were sold.

12. Write a system of equations.
    $$2x + 2y = 310$$
    $$x - y = 55$$
    Multiply one of the equations by a constant.
    $$x - y = 55$$
    $$2(x - y = 55)$$
    $$2x - 2y = 110$$
    Add the equations.
    $$2x - 2y = 110$$
    $$\underline{+2x + 2y = 310}$$
    $$4x = 420$$
    $$x = 105$$
    Substitute the value for $x$ into one of the equations.
    $$x - y = 55$$
    $$105 - y = 55$$
    $$-y = -50$$
    $$y = 50$$
    The numbers are 105 and 50. Sample answer:
    I used the system of equations $\begin{cases} 2x + 2y = 310. \\ x - y = 55 \end{cases}$
    I multiplied the second equation by 2 and added to eliminate the $y$-terms.

13. Let $x$ represent the number of pies.
Let $y$ represent the number of jars of applesauce.
Write a system of equations.
Granny Smith apples used: $5x + 4y = 169$
Golden Delicious apples used: $3x + 2y = 95$
Multiply one of the equations by a constant.
$$3x + 2y = 95$$
$$2(3x + 2y = 95)$$
$$6x + 4y = 190$$
Subtract the equations.
$$6x + 4y = 190$$
$$-(5x + 4y = 169)$$
$$x + 0 = 21$$
$$x = 21$$
Substitute the value for $x$ into one of the equations.
$$3x + 2y = 95$$
$$3(21) + 2y = 95$$
$$63 + 2y = 95$$
$$2y = 32$$
$$y = 16$$
The apples make 21 pies and 16 jars of applesauce.

## Focus on Higher Order Thinking

14. Lena's graph shows that the two lines do not intersect. This would seem to mean that the system has no solution. It would seem that solving an equation algebraically and getting a false statement means that the system has no solution.

15. a. Multiply the first equation by 1.5 and subtract. This would be less than ideal because you would introduce decimals into the solution process.

    b. Yes; multiply the first equation by 3 and the second equation by 2. Both $x$-term coefficients would be 6. Solve by eliminating the $x$-terms using subtraction.

    c. Multiply the first equation by 3.
$$2x + 3y = 6$$
$$3(2x + 3y = 6)$$
$$6x + 9y = 18$$
Multiply the second equation by 2.
$$3x + 7y = -1$$
$$2(3x + 7y = -1)$$
$$6x + 14y = -2$$
Subtract the equations.
$$6x + 14y = -2$$
$$-(6x + 9y = 18)$$
$$0 + 5y = -20$$
$$y = -4$$
Substitute the value for $y$ into one of the equations.
$$2x + 3y = 6$$
$$2x + 3(-4) = 6$$
$$2x - 12 = 6$$
$$2x = 18$$
$$x = 9$$
The solution is $(9, -4)$.

## LESSON 8.5

### Your Turn

6. Solve the system by elimination.
Multiply one of the equations by a constant.
$$-2x + 3y = 4$$
$$2(-2x + 3y = 4)$$
$$-4x + 6y = 8$$
Add the equations.
$$4x - 6y = 9$$
$$+(-4x) + 6y = 8$$
$$0 = 17$$
No solution

7. Solve the system by substitution.
Solve an equation for one variable.
$$x + 2y = 6$$
$$x = 6 - 2y$$
Substitute the expression for $x$ in the other equation and solve.
$$2(6 - 2y) - 3y = 26$$
$$12 - 4y - 3y = 26$$
$$12 - 7y = 26$$
$$-7y = 14$$
$$y = -2$$
Substitute the value for $y$ into one of the equations and solve for $x$.
$$x + 2y = 6$$
$$x + 2(-2) = 6$$
$$x - 4 = 6$$
$$x = 10$$
So, there is one solution to the system, $(10, -2)$.

8. Solve the system by elimination.
Multiply one of the equations by a constant.
$$-3x + 2y = 1$$
$$4(-3x + 2y = 1)$$
$$-12x + 8y = 4$$
Add the equations.
$$12x - 8y = -4$$
$$+ -12x + 8y = 4$$
$$0 + 0 = 0$$
Infinitely many solutions

### Guided Practice

1. System A: The graphs are parallel.
System B: The graphs intersect.
System C: The graphs are the same line.
Intersecting lines have one point in common.
Parallel lines have no point in common.
The same lines have an infinite number of points in common.
Solve each system.
System A: Solve by elimination.
Multiply one of the equations by a constant.
$$2x - y = 4$$
$$2(2x - y = 4)$$
$$4x - 2y = 8$$
Subtract the equations.
$$4x - 2y = 8$$
$$-(4x - 2y = -6)$$
$$0 + 0 = 14$$
System A has no points in common, so it has no solution.

System B: Solve by substitution.
Solve an equation for one variable.

$x + y = 6$

$\quad x = 6 - y$

Substitute the expression for $x$ in the other equation and solve.

$4(6 - y) - 2y = -6$

$24 - 4y - 2y = -6$

$\quad 24 - 6y = -6$

$\quad\quad -6y = -30$

$\quad\quad\quad y = 5$

Substitute the value for $y$ into one of the equations and solve for $x$.

$x + y = 6$

$x + 5 = 6$

$\quad x = 1$

System B has 1 point in common. That point is the solution, $(1, 5)$.

System C: Solve by elimination.
Multiply one of the equations by a constant.

$\quad 2x - y = 4$

$3(2x - y = 4)$

$\quad 6x - 3y = 12$

Subtract the equations.

$\quad 6x - 3y = 12$

$\underline{-(6x - 3y = 12)}$

$\quad\quad\quad 0 + 0 = 0$

System C has an infinite number of points in common. All ordered pairs on the line will make both equations true.

2. Solve the system by substitution.
Solve an equation for one variable.

$x - 3y = 4$

$\quad x = 4 + 3y$

Substitute the expression for $x$ in the other equation and solve.

$-5(4 + 3y) + 15y = -20$

$-20 - 15y + 15y = -20$

$\quad\quad\quad\quad\quad -20 = -20$

There are infinitely many solutions.

3. Solve the system by elimination.
Multiply one of the equations by a constant.

$\quad 3x + y = 4$

$2(3x + y = 4)$

$\quad 6x + 2y = 8$

Subtract the equations.

$\quad 6x + 2y = -4$

$\underline{-(6x + 2y = 8)}$

$\quad\quad\quad 0 = -12$

There is no solution.

4. Solve the system by elimination.
Multiply one of the equations by a constant.

$\quad 3x + 4y = -25$

$2(3x + 4y = -25)$

$\quad 6x + 8y = -50$

Subtract the equations.

$\quad 6x - 2y = -10$

$\underline{-(6x + 8y = -50)}$

$\quad -10y = 40$

$\quad\quad\quad y = -4$

Substitute the value for $y$ into one of the equations and solve for $x$.

$6x - 2y = -10$

$6x - 2(-4) = -10$

$\quad 6x + 8 = -10$

$\quad\quad 6x = -18$

$\quad\quad\quad x = -3$

The solution is $(-3, -4)$. There is one solution.

5. If your solution gives specific values for $x$ and $y$, the system has one solution, $(x, y)$. If it gives a false statement, there is no solution. If it gives a true statement, there are infinitely many solutions.

**Independent Practice**

6.

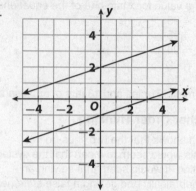

Solution: no solution
Check algebraically: Solve the system by elimination.
Multiply one of the equations by a constant.

$\quad x - 3y = 3$

$2(x - 3y = 3)$

$\quad 2x - 6y = 6$

Add the equations.

$\quad -2x + 6y = 12$

$\underline{+ 2x - 6y = 6}$

$\quad\quad\quad 0 + 0 = 18$

The algebraic check gives the same answer, no solution.

7.

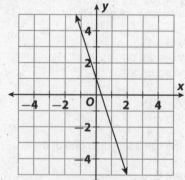

Solution: infinitely many solutions
Check algebraically: Solve the system by substitution. Solve an equation for one variable.

$3x + y = 1$

$\quad y = 1 - 3x$

Substitute the expression for $x$ in the other equation and solve.

$$15x + 5y = 5$$
$$15x + 5(1 - 3x) = 5$$
$$15x + 5 - 15x = 5$$
$$5 = 5$$

The algebraic check gives the same answer, infinitely many solutions.

8. Two linear equations with the same slopes but different $y$-intercepts are parallel lines.
No solution

9. Two linear equations with the same $y$-intercepts but different slopes are two different lines which intersect at their $y$-intercepts.
One solution

10. Two linear equations with the same $y$-intercepts and the same slopes are the same line.
Infinitely many solutions

11. Two linear equations with different $y$-intercepts and different slopes are two different lines, which are not parallel, so they must intersect.
One solution

12. The two linear equations are horizontal lines, so they are parallel and do not intersect.
No solution

13. The linear equation $x = 2$ is a vertical line. The linear equation $y = -3$ is a horizontal line. The lines intersect at the point $(2, -3)$.
One solution

14. Equation 1
$y$-intercept: $(0, 1)$
Slope: 2
Equation 2
$y$-intercept: $(0, 3)$
Slope: 2
These equations have different $y$-intercepts, but the same slope, so the lines are parallel.
No solution

15. No; although the lines do not intersect on the graph, they intersect at a point that is not on the graph. To prove that a system has no solution, you must do so algebraically.

16. Write the system of equations.
$$36x + 21y = 243$$
$$12x + 7y = 81$$
Solve the system by elimination.
Multiply one of the equations by a constant.
$$12x + 7y = 81$$
$$3(12x + 7y = 81)$$
$$36x + 21y = 243$$
Subtract the equations.
$$36x + 21y = 243$$
$$\underline{-(36x + 21y = 243)}$$
$$0 = 0$$
No, there is not enough information to find values for $x$ and $y$; there are infinitely many solutions to the system.

17. No; both Juan and Tory run at the same rate, so the lines representing the distances each has run are parallel. There is no solution to the system.

**Focus on Higher Order Thinking**

18. $m = 4$ and $b \neq -3$; the graphs of the lines must be parallel and thus must have the same slope, so $m = 4$. The $y$-intercepts must be different because two equations with the same slope and the same $y$-intercept are the same line, so $b \neq -3$.

19. $A$, $B$, and $C$ must all be the same multiple of 3, 5, and 8, respectively. The two equations represent a single line, so the coefficients and constants of one equation must be a multiple of the other.

20. The linear system has more than one solution, so the lines coincide. There are infinitely many solutions.

## MODULE 8

**Ready to Go On?**

1.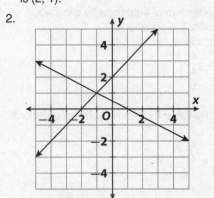

The point of intersection is $(2, 1)$. So, the solution is $(2, 1)$.

2.

The point of intersection is $(-1, 1)$. So, the solution is $(-1, 1)$.

3. To solve the system of equations by substitution, first solve one equation for one variable.
$$y = 2x$$
Substitute the expression for $y$ in the other equation and solve.
$$x + y = -9$$
$$x + (2x) = -9$$
$$3x = -9$$
$$x = -3$$

Substitute the value for $x$ into one of the equations and solve for $y$.
$$x + y = -9$$
$$-3 + y = -9$$
$$y = -6$$
The solution is $(-3, -6)$.

4. To solve the system of equations by substitution, first solve one equation for one variable.
$$x + 2y = 9$$
$$x = 9 - 2y$$
Substitute the expression for $y$ in the other equation and solve.
$$3x - 2y = 11$$
$$3(9 - 2y) - 2y = 11$$
$$27 - 6y - 2y = 11$$
$$27 - 8y = 11$$
$$-8y = -16$$
$$y = 2$$
Substitute the value for $x$ into one of the equations and solve for $y$.
$$x + 2y = 9$$
$$x + 2(2) = 9$$
$$x + 4 = 9$$
$$x = 5$$
The solution is $(5, 2)$.

5. To solve the system of equations by elimination, add or subtract the equations.
Subtract the equations.
$$3x + y = 9$$
$$-(2x + y = 5)$$
$$x = 4$$
Substitute the value for $x$ into one of the equations.
$$2x + y = 5$$
$$2(4) + y = 5$$
$$y = -3$$
The solution is $(4, -3)$.

6. To solve the system of equations by elimination, add or subtract the equations.
Add the equations.
$$-x - 2y = 4$$
$$+3x + 2y = 4$$
$$2x = 8$$
$$x = 4$$
Substitute the value for $x$ into one of the equations.
$$3x + 2y = 4$$
$$3(4) + 2y = 4$$
$$12 + 2y = 4$$
$$2y = -8$$
$$y = -4$$
The solution is $(4, -4)$.

7. Multiply one of the equations by a constant.
$$x + 3y = -2$$
$$3(x + 3y = -2)$$
$$3x + 9y = -6$$
Subtract the equations.
$$3x + 9y = -6$$
$$-(3x + 4y = -1)$$
$$0 + 5y = -5$$
$$y = -1$$

Substitute the value for $y$ into one of the equations.
$$x + 3y = -2$$
$$x + 3(-1) = -2$$
$$x - 3 = -2$$
$$x = 1$$
The solution is $(1, -1)$.

8. Multiply one of the equations by a constant.
$$3x - 2y = 5$$
$$4(3x - 2y = 5)$$
$$12x - 8y = 20$$
Add the equations.
$$2x + 8y = 22$$
$$+12x - 8y = 20$$
$$14x = 42$$
$$x = 3$$
Substitute the value for $x$ into one of the equations.
$$2x + 8y = 22$$
$$2(3) + 8y = 22$$
$$6 + 8y = 22$$
$$8y = 16$$
$$y = 2$$
The solution is $(3, 2)$.

9. Solve the system by elimination.
Multiply one of the equations by a constant.
$$x - 4y = -3$$
$$2(x - 4y = -3)$$
$$2x - 8y = -6$$
Subtract the equations.
$$-2x + 8y = 5$$
$$+2x - 8y = -6$$
$$0 = -1$$
There is no solution.

10. Solve the system by substitution.
Solve an equation for one variable.
$$x + 3y = -2$$
$$x = -2 - 3y$$
Substitute the expression for $x$ in the other equation and solve.
$$6(-2 - 3y) + 18y = -12$$
$$-12 - 18y + 18y = -12$$
$$-12 = -12$$
There are infinitely many solutions.

11. No solution: parallel lines; one solution: intersecting lines; infinitely many solutions: same line.

**MODULE 9** *Transformations and Congruence*

### Are You Ready?

1. $5 - (-9)$
   $5 + 9$
   $14$

2. $-6 - 8$
   $-14$

3. $2 - 9$
   $-7$

4. $-10 - (-6)$
   $-10 + 6$
   $-4$

5. $3 - (-11)$
   $3 + 11$
   $14$

6. $12 - 7$
   $5$

7. $-4 - 11$
   $-15$

8. $0 - (-12)$
   $0 + 12$
   $12$

9. $35°$

10. $130°$

11. $85°$

### LESSON 9.1

### Your Turn

4.

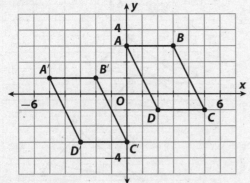

### Guided Practice

1. A transformation is a change in the position, size, or shape of a figure.

2. When you perform a transformation of a figure on the coordinate plane, the input of the transformation is called the preimage, and the output of the transformation is called the image.

3. The orientation will be the same.

4. The rectangles are congruent.

5.

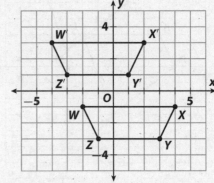

6. Sample answer: Translations preserve the size, shape, and orientation of a figure.

### Independent Practice

7. a.

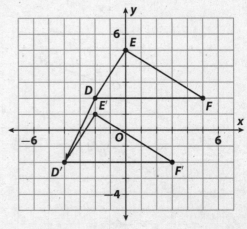

b. The translation moved the triangle 2 units to the left and 4 units down.

c. The triangles are congruent.

8. a.

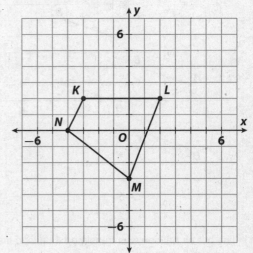

b.

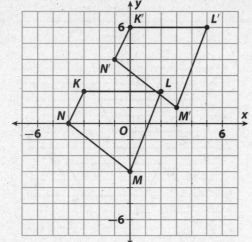

c. Side $\overline{L'M'}$ is congruent to side $\overline{LM}$.; Three other pairs of congruent sides are $\overline{KL}$ and $\overline{K'L'}$, $\overline{MN}$ and $\overline{M'N'}$, and $\overline{KN}$ and $\overline{K'N'}$.

9.

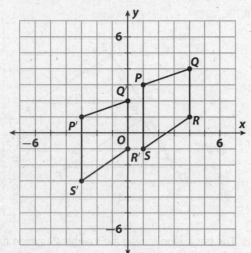

10.

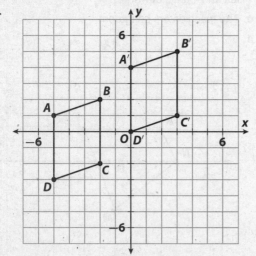

11. The hot air balloon was translated 4 units to the right and 5 units up.

12. No; When a figure is translated, it is slid to a new location. Since it is not turned or flipped, the orientation will remain the same.

## Focus on Higher Order Thinking

13. a.

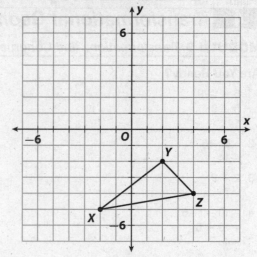

b.

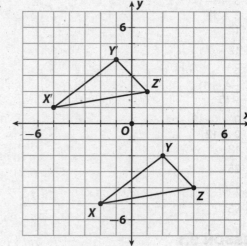

c.

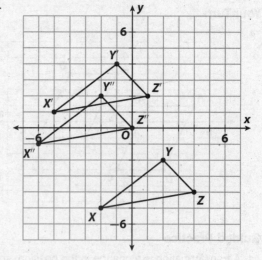

d. Sample answer: The original triangle was translated 4 units up and 4 units to the left.

14.

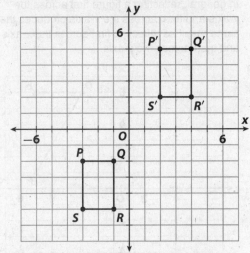

15. Sample answer: Since every point of the original figure is translated the same number of units up/down and left/right, the image is exactly the same size and shape as the preimage. Only the location is different.

## LESSON 9.2

### Your Turn

4.

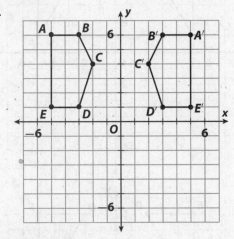

### Guided Practice

1. A reflection is a transformation that flips a figure across a line called the line of reflection.

2. a.

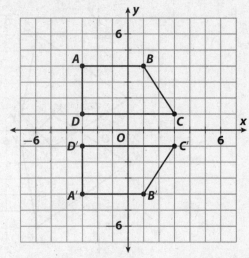

b. The trapezoids are congruent.

c. The orientation would be reversed horizontally. That is, the figure from left to right in the preimage would match the figure from right to left in the image.

3. Sample answer: Reflections preserve size and shape but not orientation.

### Independent Practice

4. Triangles A and C are reflections of each other across the x-axis.

5. The y-axis is the line of reflection for triangles C and D.

6. triangle B; Triangle B is the image of triangle C after a translation of 8 units up and 6 units right.

7. Sample answer: Since each triangle is either a reflection or translation of triangle C, they are all congruent.

8. a.

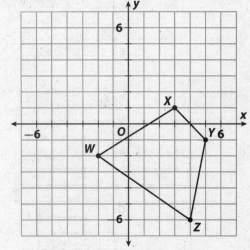

**b.**

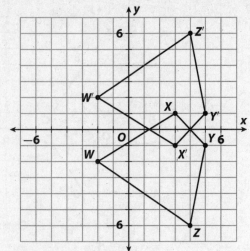

**c.** Side $\overline{Y'Z'}$ is congruent to side $\overline{YZ}$.; Three other pairs of congruent sides are $\overline{WX}$ and $\overline{W'X'}$, $\overline{XY}$ and $\overline{X'Y'}$, and $\overline{WZ}$ and $\overline{W'Z'}$.

**d.** $\angle X'$ is congruent to $\angle X$. Three other pairs of congruent angles are $\angle W$ and $\angle W'$, $\angle Y$ and $\angle Y'$, and $\angle Z$ and $\angle Z'$.

9. Yes; If the point lies on the line of reflection, then the image and the preimage will be the same point.

## Focus on Higher Order Thinking

10. **a.**

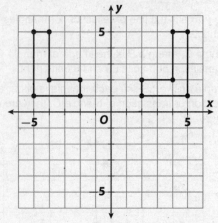

**b.**

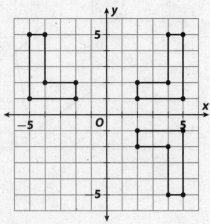

**c.** The same image can be obtained by reflecting first across the *x*-axis and then across the *y*-axis. In general, reflecting a figure first across the *y*-axis and then across the *x*-axis produces the same result as reflecting first across the *x*-axis and then across the *y*-axis.

11. **a.**

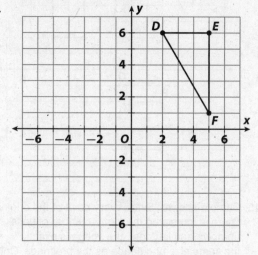

**b.**

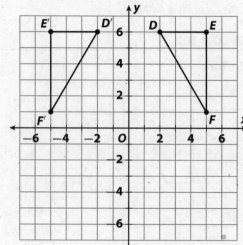

**c.**

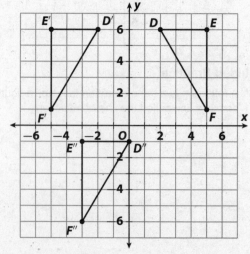

**d.** Sample answer: Translate triangle *DEF* 7 units down and 2 units to the left. Then reflect the image across the *y*-axis.

**Your Turn**

6.

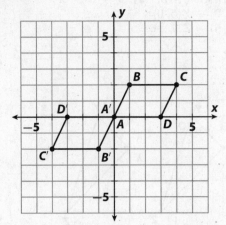

7.

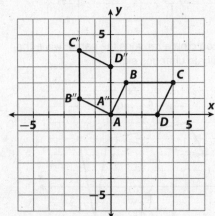

8. The image of point C after a rotation of 90°
   counterclockwise is the point (−2, 4). The image
   after this point is rotated 180° is the point (2, −4).

## Guided Practice

1. A rotation is a transformation that turns a figure
   around a given point called the center of rotation.

2. The triangle is turned 90° to the left.

3. Yes, the figures are congruent.

4.

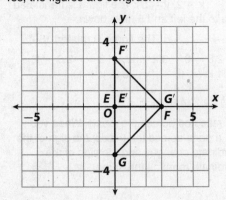

5.

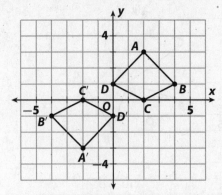

6. Sample answer: Rotations preserve size and shape
   but change orientation.

## Independent Practice

7. a. Triangle ABC was rotated 90° counterclockwise.

   b. A'(3, 1), B'(2, 3), C'(−1, 4)

8. a. The figure was rotated 180° about the origin.

   b. Yes; You can also describe it as a reflection
      across the y-axis.

9. The orientation will be preserved after a
   180° rotation.

10. The image will be the point (−3, 2).

11–13.

| Shape in quadrant | Image in quadrant | Rotation |
|---|---|---|
| I | IV | 90° clockwise |
| III | I | 180° |
| IV | III | 90° clockwise |

14.

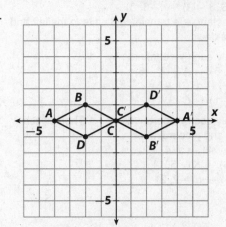

15.

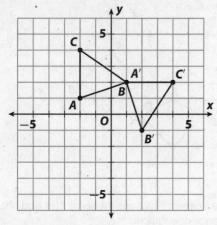

16. Yes; A rotation of 360° will produce an image with the same orientation.

## Focus on Higher Order Thinking

17. Figure A: 2 times; Figure B: 1 time, Figure C: 4 times

18. Triangle $A''B''C''$ is a 180° rotation of triangle $ABC$.

19. Sample answer: If $A$ is at the origin, $A'$ for any rotation about the origin is at the origin. Otherwise, $A'$ is on the $x$-axis for 90° and 270° rotations and on the $y$-axis for a 180° rotation.

# LESSON 9.4

## Your Turn

1. Subtract 6 from each $x$-coordinate and 3 from each $y$-coordinate.
$(0 - 6, -2 - 3) \rightarrow (-6, -5)$
$(0 - 6, 3 - 3) \rightarrow (-6, 0)$
$(3 - 6, -2 - 3) \rightarrow (-3, -5)$
$(3 - 6, 3 - 3) \rightarrow (-3, 0)$
The rectangle is translated 6 units to the left and 3 units down.

2. Multiply each $y$-coordinate by $-1$.
$A(-2, 6) \rightarrow A'(-2, -6)$
$B(0, 5) \rightarrow B'(0, -5)$
$C(3, -1) \rightarrow C'(3, 1)$

4. Multiply each $y$-coordinate by $-1$. Then switch the $x$- and $y$-coordinates.
$J(-2, -4) \rightarrow J'(4, -2)$
$K(1, 5) \rightarrow K'(-5, 1)$
$L(2, 2) \rightarrow L'(-2, 2)$

## Guided Practice

1. Add 6 to each $x$-coordinate.
$X(-3, -2) \rightarrow X'(3, -2)$
$Y(-1, 0) \rightarrow Y'(5, 0)$
$Z(1, -6) \rightarrow Z'(7, -6)$

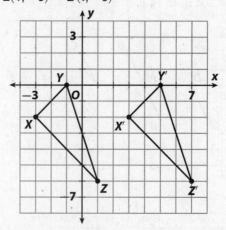

2. The $x$-coordinate remains the same, while the $y$-coordinate changes sign.

3.

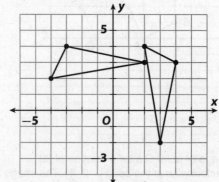

The triangle is rotated about the origin 90° clockwise.

4. The $x$-coordinates increase by $a$, and the $y$-coordinates decrease by $b$.

## Independent Practice

5. $(x, y) \rightarrow (x - 2, y - 5)$; The figure is translated 2 units to the left and 5 units down.

6. $(x, y) \rightarrow (-x, -y)$; The figure is rotated 180°.

7. Since $2.8 = 6 - 3.2$, and $-1.3 = -2.3 + 1$, the rule is $(x, y) \rightarrow (x - 3.2, y + 1)$.
$Y(7.5, 5) \rightarrow Y'(4.3, 6)$
$Z(8, 4) \rightarrow Z'(4.8, 5)$

8. It was reflected across the $y$-axis; When you reflect a point across the $y$-axis, the sign of the $x$-coordinate changes and the sign of the $y$-coordinate remains the same.

9.

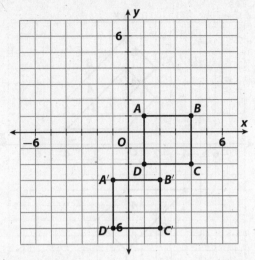

The rectangle is translated 2 units to the left and 4 units down.

10. Subtract $2\frac{1}{2}$ from each $y$-coordinate.

$$A\left(-2, -5\frac{1}{2}\right) \rightarrow A'(-2, -8)$$

$$B\left(-4, -5\frac{1}{2}\right) \rightarrow B'(-4, -8)$$

$$C(-3, -2) \rightarrow C'\left(-3, -4\frac{1}{2}\right)$$

$$D(-1, -2) \rightarrow D'\left(-1, -4\frac{1}{2}\right)$$

11. The shadow is a translation of the logo one-half inch to the right and one-quarter inch down.
$(x, y) \rightarrow (x + 0.5, y - 0.25)$

12. Since the $y$-coordinate has been multiplied by $-1$ and the coordinates have been switched, the rotation is 90° counterclockwise;
$(x, y) + (-y, x)$
$L(2, 4) + L'(-4, 2)$
$M(3, 3) + M'(-3, 3)$
$N(2, 0) + N'(0, 2)$

## Focus on Higher Order Thinking

13.

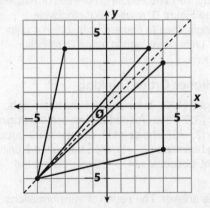

a. $(-5, -5)$; Since $x$ and $y$ are equal, switching $x$ and $y$ has no effect on the coordinates.

b. The equation of the line is $y = x$.

c. The triangle is a reflected across the line $y = x$.

14. Yes; Sample answer: Reflecting across the $x$- or $y$-axis changes the sign of the $y$- or $x$-coordinate; 0 cannot change signs. Rotating about the origin doesn't change the origin, (0, 0).

15. a. Subtracting 1 from each $x$-coordinate and then adding 4 is the same as adding 3. Adding 3 to each $y$-coordinate and then subtracting 1 is the same as adding 2.
$A(-2, -2) \rightarrow A''(1, 0)$
$B(-3, 1) \rightarrow B''(0, 3)$
$C(1, 1) \rightarrow C''(4, 3)$

b. $(x, y) \rightarrow (x + 3, y + 2)$

## LESSON 9.5

### Your Turn

3. Rotation 90° clockwise about origin, translation 5 units down; $(x, y) \rightarrow (y, -x)$, $(x, y) \rightarrow (x, y-5)$

### Guided Practice

1. a.–e.

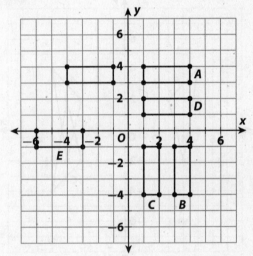

2. The transformation used is a reflection across the $y$-axis.

3. The transformation used is a translation 3 units right and 4 units down.

4. Algebraically the sequence of transformations used is $(x, y) \rightarrow (-x, y)$, $(x, y) \rightarrow (x + 3, y - 4)$.

5. The figures have the same size and the same shape.

6. They have the same size and the same shape. (They are congruent.)

## Independent Practice

**7.**

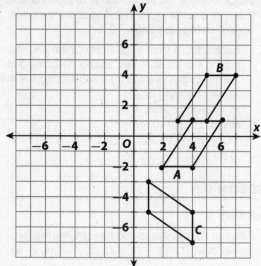

Figures *A* and *C* have different orientation.

**8.**

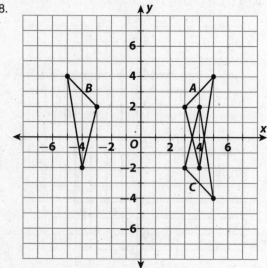

Figures *A* and *C* have different orientation.

**9.**

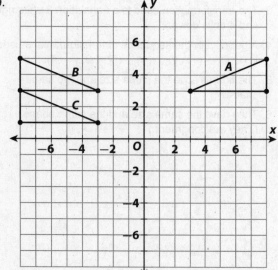

Figures *A* and *C* have different orientation.

**10.**

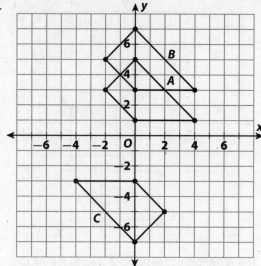

Figures *A* and *C* have different orientation.

**11.** Sample answer: To change the building site the transformations were a translation of 2 units right and 4 units down, and a reflection across the *y*-axis. The size of the library did not change, but the orientation did change.

**12.**

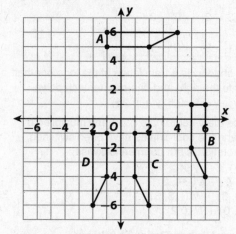

Sample answer: The sequence of transformations could be to Figure B: rotation 90° clockwise around origin; then to figure C: translation 4 units left and 2 units down; and to figure D: reflection across *y*-axis.

## Focus on Higher Order Thinking

**13.** No; the point (1, 2), translated 2 units to the right, becomes (3, 2), then rotated 90° around the origin it becomes (2, −3). The point (1, 2) rotated 90° around the origin becomes (2, −1), then translated 2 units to the right it becomes (4, −1), which is not the same.

**14. a.** Sample answer: The series of transformations could be a translation of 2 units right and 1 unit up, and a reflection across *y*-axis.

**b.** Sample answer: The series of transformations could be a rotation 90° clockwise around the origin, and a translation 3 units down.

# MODULE 9

## Ready to Go On?

1.

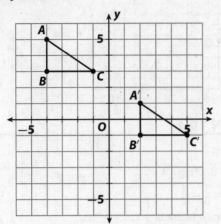

2.

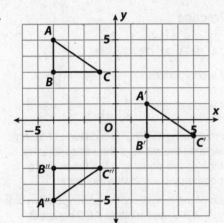

3.

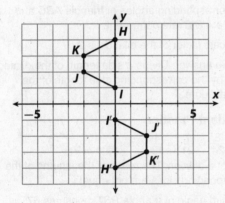

4. Add 4 to each x-coordinate and subtract 3 from each y-coordinate.
$(2 + 4, 3 - 3) \rightarrow (6, 0)$
$(-2 + 4, 2 - 3) \rightarrow (2, -1)$
$(-3 + 4, 5 - 3) \rightarrow (1, 2)$
The triangle is translated 4 units to the right and 3 units down.

5. Translations, reflections, and rotations produce a figure that is congruent to the original figure.

6.

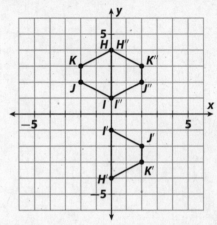

7. Sample answer: You can use transformations to determine movement from one location to another.

## MODULE 10 *Transformations and Similarity*

### Are You Ready?

1. $\frac{6}{15}$

   $\frac{6 \div 3}{15 \div 3}$

   $\frac{2}{5}$

2. $\frac{8}{20}$

   $\frac{8 \div 4}{20 \div 4}$

   $\frac{2}{5}$

3. $\frac{30}{18}$

   $\frac{30 \div 6}{18 \div 6}$

   $\frac{5}{3}$

4. $\frac{36}{30}$

   $\frac{36 \div 6}{30 \div 6}$

   $\frac{6}{5}$

5. $60 \times \frac{25}{100}$

   $= \frac{60 \times 25}{1 \times 100}$

   $= \frac{60 \times 25^{1}}{1 \times 100_{4}}$

   $= \frac{60^{15}}{4_{1}}$

   $= 15$

6. $\quad 40$
   $\underline{\times \ 3.5}$
   $\quad 200$
   $\underline{+1200}$
   $\quad 140.0 \ \text{or} \ 140$

7. $\quad 44$
   $\underline{\times \ 4.4}$
   $\quad 176$
   $\underline{+1760}$
   $\quad 193.6$

8. $24 \times \frac{8}{9}$

   $= \frac{24 \times 8}{1 \times 9}$

   $= \frac{^{8}24 \times 8}{1 \times 9_{3}}$

   $= \frac{64}{3}, \text{ or } 21\frac{1}{3}$

9–12.

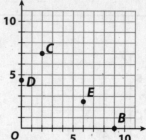

### LESSON 10.1

#### Your Turn

5. $DE = 6$, $D'E' = 3$

   $\frac{D'E'}{DE} = \frac{3}{6} = \frac{1}{2}$

   The scale factor is $\frac{1}{2}$.

#### Guided Practice

1. $A(-2, 2)$, $B(2, 1)$, $C(-1, -2)$
   $A'(-4, 4)$, $B'(4, 2)$, $C'(-2, -4)$

   ratio of *x*-coordinates $= \frac{-4}{-2} = \frac{4}{2} = \frac{-2}{-1} = 2$

   ratio of *y*-coordinates $= \frac{4}{2} = \frac{2}{1} = \frac{-4}{-2} = 2$

2. I know that triangle $A'B'C'$ is a dilation of triangle $ABC$ because the ratios of the corresponding *x*-coordinates are equal and the ratios of the corresponding *y*-coordinates are equal.

3. The ratio of the lengths of the corresponding sides of triangle $A'B'C'$ and triangle $ABC$ equals 2.

4. The corresponding angles of triangle $ABC$ and triangle $A'B'C'$ are congruent.

5. The scale factor of the dilation is 2.

6. Sample answer: Divide a side length of the dilated figure by the corresponding side length of the original figure.

#### Independent Practice

7. $\frac{5}{15} = \frac{8}{24} = \frac{7}{21} \neq \frac{4}{18}$

   It is not a dilation; The ratios of the lengths of the corresponding sides are not equal.

8. The third angle of triangle $RST$ measures 67°. The third angle of triangle $R'S'T'$ measures 75°. Therefore, it is a dilation; Both triangles have angles of measure 38°, 75°, and 67°, so the corresponding angles are congruent.

9. It is a dilation. A dilation produces an image that is similar to the original figure.

10. It is a dilation. If figures are the same shape but a different size, they are similar. Therefore, one is a dilation of the other.

11. ratio of x-coordinates $= \frac{15}{20} = \frac{6}{8} = \frac{-18}{-24} = \frac{3}{4}$

ratio of y-coordinates $= \frac{-9}{-12} = \frac{4.5}{6} = \frac{-3}{-4} = \frac{3}{4}$

It is a dilation; Each coordinate of triangle $U'V'W'$ is $\frac{3}{4}$ times the corresponding coordinate of triangle $UVW$. So, the scale factor of the dilation is $\frac{3}{4}$.

12–15.

| Image Compared to Original Figure | | | |
|---|---|---|---|
| | Orientation | Size | Shape |
| **Translation** | same | same | same |
| **Reflection** | changed | same | same |
| **Rotation** | changed | same | same |
| **Dilation** | same | changed | same |

16. The image is congruent to the original figure.

17. $AB = 2$, $A'B' = 6$

$\frac{A'B'}{AB} = \frac{6}{2} = 3$

The scale factor is 3.

18. $AB = 4$, $A'B' = 2$

$\frac{A'B'}{AB} = \frac{2}{4} = \frac{1}{2}$

The scale factor is $\frac{1}{2}$.

### Focus on Higher Order Thinking

19. Sample answer: Locate the corresponding vertices of the triangles and draw lines connecting each pair. The lines will intersect at the center of dilation.

20. a. The ratio of the coordinates of corresponding vertices is 2, so the scale factor is 2; The perimeter of the original square is 16 units, the perimeter of the image is 32 units.

b. The ratio of the coordinates of corresponding vertices is 2, so the scale factor is 2; The perimeter of the original square is 24 units; the perimeter of the image is 48 units.

c. Sample answer: The perimeter of the image is the perimeter of the original figure times the scale factor.

## LESSON 10.2

### Your Turn

5. Multiply the coordinates of each point by $\frac{1}{3}$ to find the coordinates of the image.

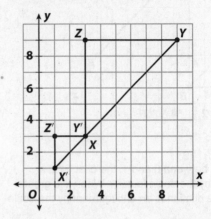

$(x, y) \rightarrow \left(\frac{1}{3}x, \frac{1}{3}y\right)$

### Guided Practice

1.

| Preimage | Image |
|---|---|
| (2, 0) | (3, 0) |
| (0, 2) | (0, 3) |
| (−2, 0) | (−3, 0) |
| (0, −2) | (0, −3) |

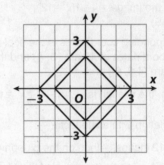

2.

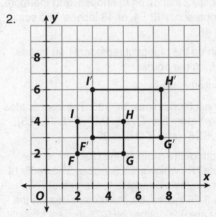

$(x, y) \rightarrow (1.5x, 1.5y)$

3.

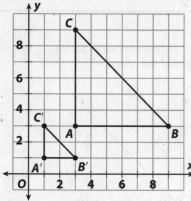

$$(x, y) \rightarrow \left(\frac{1}{3}x, \frac{1}{3}y\right)$$

4. When $k$ is between 0 and 1, the dilation is a reduction by the scale factor $k$. When $k$ is greater than 1, the dilation is an enlargement by the scale factor $k$.

## Independent Practice

5. Since the coordinates of the vertices of the green square are twice that of the blue square, the dilation is $(x, y) \rightarrow (2x, 2y)$. Since the coordinates of the vertices of the purple square are one-half that of the blue square, the dilation is $(x, y) \rightarrow \left(\frac{1}{2}x, \frac{1}{2}y\right)$.

6. Multiply the coordinates of each point by 3 to find the coordinates of the image: $A'(-15, -12)$, $B'(6, 18)$, $C'(12, -9)$

7. The ratio of corresponding coordinates is the scale factor. Since the coordinates of $M'$ are $(3, 4)$ and the coordinates of $M$ are $(4.5, 6)$, and since $\frac{3}{4.5} = \frac{4}{6} = \frac{2}{3}$, the dilation is $(x, y) \rightarrow \left(\frac{2}{3}x, \frac{2}{3}y\right)$.

8. You can apply a dilation with scale factor $\frac{1}{k}$.

9. a. Since 1 foot = 12 inches, $\frac{1}{4}$ inch on the blueprint represents 12 inches on the house, and therefore, 1 inch represents $12 \cdot 4$, or 48 inches. The scale factor is 48.

   b. One inch on the blueprint represents 48 inches, or 4 feet, on the house.

   c. $(x, y) \rightarrow (48x, 48y)$

   d. Multiply each coordinate by 1.25. The coordinates of the new room are: $Q'(2.5, 2.5)$, $R'(8.75, 2.5)$, $S'(8.75, 6.25)$, and $T'(2.5, 6.25)$.

   e. The length of the room on the blueprint is the length of $Q'R'$, which is 6.25 inches. The width of the room on the blueprint is the length of $R'S'$, which is 3.75 inches. So, the dimensions on the blueprint are 6.25 inches by 3.75 inches. Multiply by 48 to find the dimensions of the room in inches. Divide each result by 12 to find the measurement in feet.
   $(6.25 \times 48) \div 12 = 25$
   $(3.75 \times 48) \div 12 = 15$
   The dimensions of the room are 25 feet by 15 feet.

10. Since the coordinates of the vertices of the image are one-quarter that of the preimage, the dilation is $(x, y) \rightarrow \left(\frac{1}{4}x, \frac{1}{4}y\right)$.

## Focus on Higher Order Thinking

11. The crewmember's calculation is incorrect; The scale factor for the backdrop is $\frac{20}{400}$, or $\frac{1}{20}$, not $\frac{1}{12}$.

12. a. This transformation rotates the figure 90° clockwise.

    b. This transformation rotates the figure 180°.

    c. This transformation stretches the figure vertically by a factor of 2.

    d. This transformation shrinks the figure horizontally by a factor of $\frac{2}{3}$.

    e. This transformation shrinks the figure horizontally by a factor of 0.5, and stretches the figure vertically by a factor of 1.5.

13.

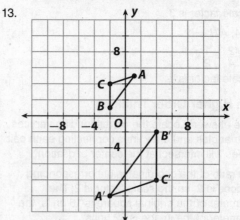

The figure is dilated by a factor of 2 and rotated 180°.

## LESSON 10.3

### Your Turn

3. Sample answer: The sequence of transformation could be:$(x, y) \rightarrow (x + 7, y - 12)$; rotation 90° clockwise about the origin; $(x, y) \rightarrow (x + 5, y + 3)$; $(x, y) \rightarrow (3x, 3y)$

## Guided Practice

1.

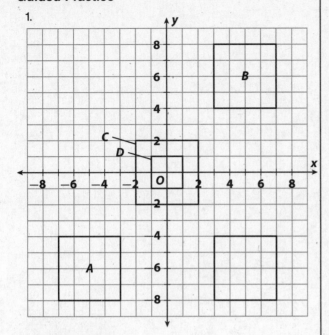

2. Sample answer:
   Transformation 1 $(x, y) \rightarrow (x, -y)$;
   Transformation 2 $(x, y) \rightarrow (x + 5, y - 6)$

3. Sample answer:
   Transformation 1 $(x, y) \rightarrow (x, y + 6)$;
   Transformation 2 rotate 90° counterclockwise

4. Sample answer:
   Transformation 1 $(x, y) \rightarrow (1.5x, 1.5y)$;
   Transformation 2 $(x, y) \rightarrow (x + 3, y + 5)$

5. At least one transformation must be a dilation.

## Independent Practice

6. a. To find the length of each side of the actual sign multiply each side of the drawing by the scale factor.
      $6 \times 40 = 240$ cm
      $8 \times 40 = 320$ cm
      $10 \times 40 = 400$ cm
      The lengths of the sides of the actual sign are 240 cm, 320 cm, and 400 cm.
   b. The shape of a figure does not change in a dilation, so the angles remain the same.
      The angles of the actual sign are 37°, 53°, and 90°.
   c. Two transformations that would put the hypotenuse on the top: Reflect the drawing over the x-axis; rotate the drawing 180° around the origin.
   d. Reflection over the x-axis will leave the shorter leg on the left.

7. Dilate the image by a scale factor of $\frac{1}{3}$ and reflect it back across the x-axis; $(x, y) \rightarrow \left(\frac{1}{3}x, \frac{1}{3}y\right)$, $(x, y) \rightarrow (x, -y)$.

8. Translate the image 3 units down and 6 units right and dilate it by a factor of 2. $(x, y) \rightarrow (x + 6, y - 3)$, $(x, y) \rightarrow (2x, 2y)$.

9. Rotate the image 90° counterclockwise and dilate it by a factor of $\frac{1}{5}$; $(x, y) \rightarrow (-y, x)$, $(x, y) \rightarrow \left(\frac{1}{5}x, \frac{1}{5}y\right)$.

10. Dilate the image by a scale factor of $\frac{1}{4}$ and reflect it back across the y-axis; $(x, y) \rightarrow \left(\frac{1}{4}x, \frac{1}{4}y\right)$, $(x, y) \rightarrow (-x, y)$.

## Focus on Higher Order Thinking

11. There can be an even number of dilations in pairs where each has the opposite effect.

12. a. The graph remains that of $y = x$, since each transformed point is still on the line: $(0, 0) \rightarrow (0, 0)$, $(-1, -1) \rightarrow (-4, -4)$, $(1, 1) \rightarrow (4, 4)$, and so on.
    b. The y-intercept moves from 0 to −3, but the slope stays the same. The new equation is $y = x - 3$.
    c. The graph still goes through $(0, 0)$, but $(1, 1) \rightarrow (-1, 1)$, so the slope is −1. The equation is $y = -x$.

13. No; dilating first gives $(0, 0) \rightarrow (0, 0) \rightarrow (0, 5)$ and $(1, 1) \rightarrow (3, 3) \rightarrow (3, 8)$, so the transformed points are on $y = x + 5$; translating first gives $(0, 0) \rightarrow (0, 5) \rightarrow (0, 15)$ and $(1, 1) \rightarrow (1, 6) \rightarrow (3, 18)$, so the transformed points are on $y = x + 15$.

## MODULE 10

### Ready to Go On?

1. The third angle of triangle XYZ measures 97°. The third angle of triangle X′Y′Z′ measures 59°. Therefore, it is not a dilation since the triangles have only one pair of congruent angles.

2. $\frac{20}{16} = \frac{35}{28} = \frac{30}{24} = \frac{25}{20} = \frac{5}{4}$

   It is a dilation; The ratios of the lengths of the corresponding sides are equal.

3.

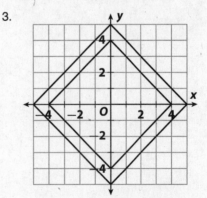

4.

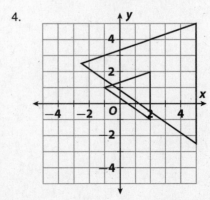

5. $(x, y) \rightarrow (-x, y)$ is a rexflection over the $y$-axis.

   $(x, y) \rightarrow (0.5x, 0.5y)$ is a dilation with a scale factor of 0.5.

   $(x, y) \rightarrow (x - 2, y + 2)$ is a translation 2 units left and 2 units up.

6. Sample answer: You can use dilations when drawing blueprints for a room or house.

# Solutions Key
## *Measurement Geometry*

**MODULE 11** *Angle Relationships in Parallel Lines and Triangles*

### Are You Ready?

1.  $6x + 10 = 46$
    $6x + 10 - 10 = 46 - 10$
    $6x = 36$
    $\dfrac{6x}{6} = \dfrac{36}{6}$
    $x = 6$

2.  $7x - 6 = 36$
    $7x - 6 + 6 = 36 + 6$
    $7x = 42$
    $\dfrac{7x}{7} = \dfrac{42}{7}$
    $x = 6$

3.  $3x + 26 = 59$
    $3x + 26 - 26 = 59 - 26$
    $3x = 33$
    $\dfrac{3x}{3} = \dfrac{33}{3}$
    $x = 11$

4.  $2x + 5 = -25$
    $2x + 5 - 5 = -25 - 5$
    $2x = -30$
    $\dfrac{2x}{2} = \dfrac{-30}{2}$
    $x = -15$

5.  $6x - 7 = 41$
    $6x - 7 + 7 = 41 + 7$
    $6x = 48$
    $\dfrac{6x}{6} = \dfrac{48}{6}$
    $x = 8$

6.  $\dfrac{1}{2}x + 9 = 30$
    $\dfrac{1}{2}x + 9 - 9 = 30 - 9$
    $\dfrac{1}{2}x = 21$
    $(2)\dfrac{1}{2}x = (2)21$
    $x = 42$

7.  $\dfrac{1}{3}x - 7 = 15$
    $\dfrac{1}{3}x - 7 + 7 = 15 + 7$
    $\dfrac{1}{3}x = 22$
    $(3)\dfrac{1}{3}x = (3)22$
    $x = 66$

8.  $0.5x - 0.6 = 8.4$
    $0.5x - 0.6 + 0.6 = 8.4 + 0.6$
    $0.5x = 9.0$
    $\dfrac{0.5x}{0.5} = \dfrac{9.0}{0.5}$
    $x = 18$

9.  $\angle MHR$ or $\angle RHM$

10. $\angle SGK$ or $\angle KGS$

11. $\angle BTF$ or $\angle FTB$

### LESSON 11.1

**Your Turn**

5.  Since $\angle DEH$ and $\angle BEF$ are vertical angles, $m\angle DEH = 6x°$. Since $\angle GDE$ and $\angle DEH$ are same-side interior angles, they are supplementary.
    $m\angle GDE + m\angle DEH = 180°$
    $4x° + 6x° = 180°$
    $10x = 180$
    $x = 18$
    $m\angle GDE = 4x = (4 \cdot 18)° = 72°$
    $m\angle GDE = 72°$

6.  $m\angle BEF = 6x = (6 \cdot 18)° = 108°$
    $m\angle BEF = 108°$

7.  Since $\angle CDG$ and $\angle BEF$ are alternate exterior angles, they are congruent. Since $m\angle BEF = 108°$, $m\angle CDG = 108°$.

**Guided Practice**

1.  $\angle VWZ$

2.  alternate interior

3.  Since $\angle SVW$ and $\angle TWV$ are same-side interior angles, they are supplementary.
    $m\angle SVW + m\angle TWV = 180°$
    $4x° + 5x° = 180°$
    $9x = 180$
    $x = 20$
    $m\angle SVW = 4x = (4 \cdot 20)° = 80°$
    $m\angle SVW = 80°$

4.  $m\angle VWT = 5x = (5 \cdot 20)° = 100°$
    $m\angle VWT = 100°$

5.  same-side interior

6.  Each pair of alternate interior angles is congruent. Each pair of same-side interior angles is supplementary.

**Independent Practice**

7.  $\angle 1$ and $\angle 5$, $\angle 2$ and $\angle 6$, $\angle 3$ and $\angle 7$, $\angle 4$ and $\angle 8$

8.  $\angle 1$ and $\angle 8$, $\angle 2$ and $\angle 7$

9.  alternate interior angles

10. same-side interior angles

11. Since $\angle AGE$ and $\angle FHD$ are alternate exterior angles, they are congruent. $m\angle AGE = 30°$

12. Since ∠AGH and ∠CHF are corresponding angles, they are congruent. m∠AGH = 150°

13. Since ∠CHF and ∠BGE are alternate exterior angles, they are congruent. m∠CHF = 110°

14. Since ∠CHG and ∠HGA are same-side interior angles, they are supplementary. m∠CHG = 60°

15. Since ∠BGH and ∠GHD are same-side interior angles, they are supplementary.
$$m\angle BGH + m\angle GHD = 180°$$
$$3x° + (2x + 50)° = 180°$$
$$5x + 50 = 180$$
$$5x = 130$$
$$x = 26$$
$$m\angle BGH = 4x = (3 \cdot 26)° = 78°$$
$$m\angle BGH = 78°$$

16. $$m\angle GHD = (2x + 50)° = (2 \cdot 26 + 50)° = 102°$$
$$m\angle GHD = 102°$$

17. 132°; the angle is supplementary to the 48° angle because the two angles are same-side interior angles.

18. 12 angles; at most, there would be two different angle measures. If the transversal were perpendicular to the three parallel lines, there would only be one angle measure, 90°.

19. Since ∠6 and ∠2 are corresponding angles, m∠2 = 125°. Since ∠6 and ∠3 are alternate interior angles, m∠3 = 125°. Since ∠3 and ∠7 are corresponding angles, m∠7 = 125°. Since ∠6 and ∠4 are same-side interior angles, m∠4 = 180° − 125° = 55°. Since ∠4 and ∠8 are corresponding angles, m∠8 = 55°. Since ∠4 and ∠5 are alternate interior angles, m∠5 = 55°. Since ∠5 and ∠1 are corresponding angles, m∠1 = 55°.

## Focus on Higher Order Thinking

20. Yes. Since the angles are supplementary and have the same measure, each angle measure is one-half of 180°, or 90°.
$$3x + 3x = 180$$
$$6x = 180$$
$$x = 30$$
So, $3x° = (3 \cdot 30)° = 90°$.

21. For any pair of parallel lines cut by a transversal, 3 of the other 7 angles will be congruent to the selected angle; 4 will be supplementary to the selected angle; No.

22. No. For the lines to be parallel, ∠2 and ∠3 must be 90° angles. For them to be 90°, they must be supplementary angles but the problem does not state this fact, and Aiden cannot assume it to be true.

## LESSON 11.2

### Your Turn

4. Use the Triangle Sum Theorem.
$$m\angle J + m\angle K + m\angle L = 180°$$
$$71° + m\angle K + 56° = 180°$$
$$m\angle K + 127° = 180°$$
$$m\angle K = 53°$$

5. Use the Triangle Sum Theorem.
$$m\angle R + m\angle S + m\angle T = 180°$$
$$m\angle R + 29° + 61° = 180°$$
$$m\angle R + 90° = 180°$$
$$m\angle R = 90°$$

8. Use the Exterior Angle Theorem.
$$m\angle M + m\angle N = m\angle MPQ$$
$$(5y + 3)° + (4y + 8)° = 146°$$
$$9y + 11 = 146$$
$$9y = 135$$
$$y = 15$$
$$m\angle M = (5 \cdot 15 + 3)° = 78°$$
$$m\angle N = (4 \cdot 15 + 8)° = 68°$$

### Guided Practice

1. Use the Triangle Sum Theorem.
$$m\angle L + m\angle M + m\angle N = 180°$$
$$78° + m\angle M + 31° = 180°$$
$$m\angle M + 109° = 180°$$
$$m\angle M = 71°$$

2. Use the Triangle Sum Theorem.
$$m\angle Q + m\angle R + m\angle S = 180°$$
$$m\angle Q + 126° + 24° = 180°$$
$$m\angle Q + 150° = 180°$$
$$m\angle Q = 30°$$

3. $$m\angle T + m\angle U + m\angle V = 180°$$
$$(7x + 4)° + (2x + 5)° + (5x + 3)° = 180°$$
$$14x + 12 = 180$$
$$14x = 168$$
$$x = 12$$
$$m\angle T = (7 \cdot 12 + 4)° = 88°$$
$$m\angle U = (2 \cdot 12 + 5)° = 29°$$
$$m\angle V = (5 \cdot 12 + 3)° = 63°$$

4. $$m\angle X + m\angle Y + m\angle Z = 180°$$
$$n° + \left(\frac{1}{2}n\right)° + \left(\frac{1}{2}n\right)° = 180°$$
$$2n = 180$$
$$n = 90$$
$$m\angle X = 90°$$
$$m\angle Y = \left(\frac{1}{2} \cdot 90\right)° = 45°$$
$$m\angle Z = \left(\frac{1}{2} \cdot 90\right)° = 45°$$

5.     $m\angle C + m\angle D = m\angle DEF$
$(4y)° + (7y + 6)° = 116°$
$11y + 6 = 116$
$11y = 110$
$y = 10$
$m\angle C = (4 \cdot 10)° = 40°$
$m\angle D = (7 \cdot 10 + 6)° = 76°$
$m\angle DEC = 180° - (40° + 76°) = 64°$

6.     $m\angle JKM + m\angle LKM = 180°$
$161° + m\angle LKM = 180$
$161° - 161° + m\angle LKM = 180° - 161°$
$m\angle LKM = 19°$
Use the Triangle Sum Theorem.
$m\angle LKM + m\angle L + m\angle M = 180°$
$19° + (18z + 3)° + (5z - 3)° = 180°$
$23z + 19 = 180$
$23z = 161$
$z = 7$
$m\angle L = (18 \cdot 7 + 3)° = 129°$
$m\angle M = (5 \cdot 7 - 3)° = 32°$

7. The sum of the interior angles is 180°. The measure of an exterior angle equals the sum of the measures of its two remote interior angles.

## Independent Practice

8. Use the Triangle Sum Theorem.
$m\angle D + m\angle E + m\angle F = 180°$
$98° + x° + x° = 180°$
$2x + 98 = 180$
$2x = 82$
$x = 41$
$m\angle E = 41°$
$m\angle F = 41°$

9. Use the Triangle Sum Theorem.
$m\angle T + m\angle V + m\angle W = 180°$
$2x° + x° + 90° = 180°$
$3x + 90 = 180$
$3x = 90$
$x = 30$
$m\angle T = 2 \cdot 30° = 60°$
$m\angle V = 30°$

10. Use the Triangle Sum Theorem.
$m\angle G + m\angle H + m\angle J = 180°$
$5x° + 4x° + 3x° = 180°$
$12x = 180$
$x = 15$
$m\angle G = 5 \cdot 15° = 75°$
$m\angle H = 4 \cdot 15° = 60°$
$m\angle J = 3 \cdot 15° = 45°$

11. Use the Exterior Angle Theorem.
    $m\angle P + m\angle Q = m\angle QRS$
$(2y - 7)° + (3y + 5)° = 153°$
$5y - 2 = 153$
$5y = 155$
$y = 31$
$m\angle Q = (3 \cdot 31 + 5)° = 98°$
$m\angle P = (2 \cdot 31 - 7)° = 55°$
$m\angle QRP = (180 - 153)° = 27°$

12. Use the Triangle Sum Theorem.
$m\angle A + m\angle B + m\angle ACB = 180°$
$78° + 58° + m\angle ACB = 180°$
$136° + m\angle ACB = 180°$
$m\angle ACB = 44°$
Use the Exterior Angle Theorem.
$m\angle D + m\angle E = m\angle ACD$
$85° + 60° = 44° + m\angle BCD$
$145° = 44° + m\angle BCD$
$101° = m\angle BCD$
Use the Triangle Sum Theorem.
$m\angle DCE + m\angle D + m\angle E = 180°$
$m\angle DCE + 85° + 60° = 180°$
$m\angle DCE + 145° = 180°$
$m\angle DCE = 35°$

13. Use the Triangle Sum Theorem.
$m\angle K + m\angle L + m\angle KML = 180°$
$2x° + 3x° + x° = 180°$
$6x = 180$
$x = 30$
$m\angle K = (2 \cdot 30)° = 60°$
$m\angle L = (3 \cdot 30)° = 90°$
$m\angle KML = 30°$
$m\angle LMN = 60° + 90° = 150°$

14. Use the Triangle Sum Theorem.
Let $x° =$ the measure of the first angle.
Let $5x° =$ the measure of the second angle.

Let $\frac{2}{3}x° =$ the measure of the third angle.

$x° + 5x° + \frac{2}{3}x° = 180°$

$6\frac{2}{3}x = 180$

$\frac{20}{3}x = 180$

$x = 27$
$5 \cdot 27° = 135°$

$\frac{2}{3} \cdot 27° = 18°$

The angle measures are 27°, 135°, and 18°.

15. No; The measure of an obtuse angle is greater than 90°. If a triangle had two obtuse angles, the sum of their measures would be greater than 180°, yet the sum of the measures of the three angles of a triangle must equal 180°.

## Focus on Higher Order Thinking

16. The angles of an equilateral triangle are congruent. Let the measure of each angle equal $x$. Then, by the Triangle Sum Theorem, $x + x + x = 180$. So, $3x = 180$. Solving for $x$ gives $x = 60$. So the measure of each angle is 60°.

17. a. The diagonal would divide the quadrilateral into 2 triangles. Since the sum of the measures of the angles of each triangle is 180°, the sum of the measures of the angles of the quadrilateral is $2 \cdot 180°$, or 360°.

**89**

b. The sum of the angle measures of a quadrilateral is 360°; Sample answer: Any quadrilateral can be divided into two triangles. So, the sum of the angle measures of a quadrilateral is twice the sum of the angle measures of a triangle, $2 \cdot 180°$, which is 360°.

18. (1) The measure of an exterior angle is equal to the sum of the measures of its two remote interior angles. (2) An exterior angle is supplementary to the interior angle adjacent to it.

## LESSON 11.3

### Your Turn

3. The measure of the missing angle in the first triangle is $180° - (70° + 58°) = 52°$.

The measure of the missing angle in the first triangle is $180° - (70° + 49°) = 61°$.

The triangles are not similar because their angles are not congruent. The angle measures of the first triangle are 70°, 58°, and 52°. The angle measures of the second triangle are 70°, 61°, and 49°. To prove similarity you need to show that two angles in each triangle are equal.

5. $\dfrac{8}{24} = \dfrac{h}{2}$

$24h = 16$

$h = \dfrac{16}{24}$

$h = \dfrac{2}{3}$

$\dfrac{2}{3}$ ft $= \left(\dfrac{2}{3} \cdot 12\right)$ in. $= 8$ in.

The support piece is 8 inches long.

6. Let $h$ represent the height of the tree.

$\dfrac{6}{16} = \dfrac{h}{56}$

$16h = 336$

$h = 21$

The tree is 21 feet tall.

### Guided Practice

1. The measure of the missing angle in the first triangle is $180° - (41° + 30°) = 109°$.

The measure of the missing angle in the first triangle is $180° - (109° + 30°) = 41°$.

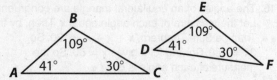

$\triangle ABC$ has angle measures 41°, 109°, and 30° and $\triangle DEF$ has angle measures 41°, 109°, and 30°. Because two angles in one triangle are congruent to two angles in the other triangle, the triangles are similar.

2. $\dfrac{5.5}{7.5} = \dfrac{h}{23.5}$

$7.5h = 129.25$

$h = 17.2\overline{3}$

The flagpole is 17.2 feet long.

3. $\angle BAC$ and $\angle EDC$ are congruent since they are alternate interior angles. $\angle ABC$ and $\angle DEC$ are congruent since they are alternate interior angles. By AA Similarity, $\triangle ABC$ and $\triangle DEC$ are similar.

4. If two angles of one triangle are congruent to two angles of the other triangle, the triangles are similar by the Angle–Angle Similarity Postulate.

### Independent Practice

5. $m\angle B = 180° - (85° + 53°) = 42°$.
$m\angle F = 180° - (47° + 64°) = 69°$
$m\angle H = 180° - (47° + 69°) = 64°$
$m\angle K = 180° - (85° + 42°) = 53°$

6. $\triangle ABC$ and $\triangle JLK$ are similar. $\triangle DEF$ and $\triangle HGI$ are similar.

7. $\angle J \cong \angle A$, $\angle L \cong \angle B$, and $\angle K \cong \angle C$

8. a. Let $h$ represent the height of the tree.

$\dfrac{6}{4} = \dfrac{h}{20}$

$4h = 120$

$h = 30$

The tree is 30 feet tall.

b. $30 - 6 = 24$. The tree is 24 feet taller than Frank.

9.

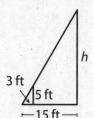

Let $h$ represent the height of the top of the ladder.

$\dfrac{5}{3} = \dfrac{h}{15}$

$3h = 75$

$h = 25$

The top of the ladder is 25 feet from the ground.

10. Yes; Each angle of an equilateral triangle measures 60°, so all three angles of one equilateral triangle are congruent to all three angles of any other equilateral triangle.

11. In the first line, Ryan should have added 19.5 and 6.5 to get a denominator of 26 for the expression on the right side. Doing so gives the correct value of 13.6 cm for $h$.

### Focus on Higher Order Thinking

12. The earrings are similar if two angle measures of one are equal to two angle measures of the other. They are congruent if they are similar and if the side lengths of one are equal to the side lengths of the other.

13. Sample answer: Using similar triangles is useful when the item is too tall or too large to measure with a tape measure or other measuring device, or if a straight-line path is not accessible.

14. No; Unless the original triangle was isosceles, the side lengths will no longer be proportional. For example, a right triangle with side lengths 3, 4, and 5 units is similar to a right triangle with side lengths 6, 8, and 10 units. If the legs of both triangles are extended by 1 unit, the lengths of the legs become 4 and 5, and 7 and 9, and $\frac{7}{4} \neq \frac{9}{5}$.

## MODULE 11

### Ready to Go On?

1. Since $\angle 7$ is supplementary to $\angle 8$, $m\angle 7 = 65°$.

2. Since $\angle 6$ and $\angle 8$ are corresponding angles, $m\angle 6 = 115°$.

3. Since $\angle 1$ and $\angle 8$ are alternate exterior angles, $m\angle 1 = 115°$.

4. Use the Exterior Angle Theorem.
$$m\angle A + m\angle B = m\angle BCD$$
$$4y° + (3y + 22)° = 106°$$
$$7y + 22 = 106$$
$$7y = 84$$
$$y = 12$$
$$m\angle A = (4 \cdot 12)° = 48°$$

5. $m\angle B = (3 \cdot 12 + 22)° = 58°$

6. $m\angle BCA = 180° - 106° = 74°$

7. 
$$\frac{EG}{HJ} = \frac{FG}{IJ}$$

$$\frac{42}{x + 12} = \frac{60}{40}$$
$$60(x + 12) = 1,680$$
$$60x + 720 = 1,680$$
$$60x = 960$$
$$x = 16$$

8. 
$$m\angle J = m\angle G$$
$$(5y + 7)° = 52°$$
$$5y = 45$$
$$y = 9$$

9. $m\angle H = m\angle E$
$$m\angle E = 180° - (52° + 36°) = 92°$$
$$m\angle H = 92°$$

10. Sample answer: You can find lengths that you can't measure directly.

## MODULE 12 *The Pythagorean Theorem*

### Are You Ready?

1. $5 \times 5 = 25$

2. $16 \times 16 = 256$

3. $(-11) \times (-11) = 121$

4. $\frac{2}{7} \times \frac{2}{7}$

   $\frac{4}{49}$

5. $\sqrt{(6+2)^2 + (3+3)^2}$

   $\sqrt{(8)^2 + (6)^2}$

   $\sqrt{64 + 36}$

   $\sqrt{100}$

   $10$

6. $\sqrt{(9-4)^2 + (5+7)^2}$

   $\sqrt{(5)^2 + (12)^2}$

   $\sqrt{25 + 144}$

   $\sqrt{169}$

   $13$

7. $\sqrt{(10-6)^2 + (15-12)^2}$

   $\sqrt{(4)^2 + (3)^2}$

   $\sqrt{16 + 9}$

   $\sqrt{25}$

   $5$

8. $\sqrt{(6+9)^2 + (10-2)^2}$

   $\sqrt{(15)^2 + (8)^2}$

   $\sqrt{225 + 64}$

   $\sqrt{289}$

   $17$

9. $5(8)(10)$

   $40(10)$

   $400$

10. $\frac{1}{2}(6)(12)$

    $3(12)$

    $36$

11. $\frac{1}{3}(3)(12)$

    $1(12)$

    $12$

12. $\frac{1}{2}(8)^2(4)$

    $\frac{1}{2}(64)(4)$

    $32(4)$

    $128$

13. $\frac{1}{4}(10)^2(15)$

    $\frac{1}{4}(100)(15)$

    $25(15)$

    $375$

14. $\frac{1}{3}(9)^2(6)$

    $\frac{1}{3}(81)(6)$

    $27(6)$

    $162$

### LESSON 12.1

**Your Turn**

4. $a^2 + b^2 = c^2$

   $30^2 + 40^2 = c^2$

   $900 + 1{,}600 = c^2$

   $2{,}500 = c^2$

   $50 = c$

   The length of the hypotenuse is 50 ft.

5. $a^2 + b^2 = c^2$

   $a^2 + 40^2 = 41^2$

   $a^2 + 1{,}600 = 1{,}681^2$

   $a^2 = 81^2$

   $a = 9$

   The length of the leg is 9 in.

6. First find the value of $s^2$.

   $4^2 + 14^2 = s^2$

   $16 + 196 = s^2$

   $212 = s^2$

   Use this value to find $r$.

   $4^2 + s^2 = r^2$

   $16 + 212 = r^2$

   $228 = r^2$

   $\sqrt{228} = r$

   $15.1 \approx r$

   The greatest length is 15 in.

## Guided Practice

1. $a^2 + b^2 = c^2$

   $24^2 + 10^2 = c^2$

   $676 = c^2$

   The length of the hypotenuse is 26 ft.

2. a. Let $s$ represent the length of the diagonal across the bottom of the box.

   $10^2 + 40^2 = s^2$

   $100 + 1,600 = s^2$

   $1,700 = s^2$

   The square of the length of the diagonal across the bottom of the box is 1,700 sq in.

   b. Let $r$ represent the length of the diagonal from a bottom corner to the opposite top corner.

   Use the value of $s^2$ to find $r$.

   $10^2 + s^2 = r^2$

   $100 + 1,700 = r^2$

   $1,800 = r^2$

   $\sqrt{1,800} = r$

   $42.4 \approx r$

   The length is approximately 42.4 in.; yes, the fishing rod will fit.

3. For a right triangle with legs of lengths $a$ and $b$ and hypotenuse of length $c$, $a^2 + b^2 = c^2$. You can use it to find the length of a side of a right triangle when the lengths of the other two sides are known.

## Independent Practice

4. $a^2 + b^2 = c^2$

   $4^2 + 8^2 = c^2$

   $16 + 64 = c^2$

   $80 = c^2$

   $\sqrt{80} = c$

   $8.9 \approx c$

   The length of the hypotenuse is approximately 8.9 cm.

5. $a^2 + b^2 = c^2$

   $a^2 + 8^2 = 14^2$

   $a^2 + 64 = 196$

   $a^2 = 132$

   $a = \sqrt{132}$

   $a \approx 11.5$

   The length of the leg is approximately 11.5 in.

6. Let $h$ represent the height of the screen.

   $h^2 + 132^2 = 152^2$

   $h^2 + 17,424 = 23,104$

   $h^2 = 5,680$

   $h = \sqrt{5,680}$

   $h \approx 75.4$

   The height is approximately 75.4 cm.

7. Let $h$ represent the length of the hypotenuse.

   $10^2 + 10^2 = h^2$

   $100 + 100 = h^2$

   $200 = h^2$

   $\sqrt{200} = h$

   $14.1 \approx h$

   The length of the hypotenuse is approximately 14.1 in.

8. Let $h$ represent the height of the ladder.

   $h^2 + 8^2 = 24^2$

   $h^2 + 64 = 576$

   $h^2 = 512$

   $h = \sqrt{512}$

   $h \approx 22.6$

   The ladder can reach approximately 22.6 ft.

9. First find the value of $s^2$.

   $2^2 + 12^2 = s^2$

   $4 + 144 = s^2$

   $148 = s^2$

   Use this value to find $r$.

   $2^2 + s^2 = r^2$

   $4 + 148 = r^2$

   $152 = r^2$

   $\sqrt{152} = r$

   $12.3 \approx r$

   The length of the longest flagpole that will fit is 12 ft.

10. Let $d$ represent the length of the diagonal.

    $100^2 + \left(53\frac{1}{3}\right)^2 = d^2$

    $10,000 + 2844.\overline{4} = d^2$

    $12,844.\overline{4} = d^2$

    $\sqrt{12,844.\overline{4}} = d$

    $113.\overline{3} = d$

    The length of the diagonal across the field is approximately 113 yards, which is less than 120 yards.

11. Let $t$ represent the length of the top part of the tree.

    $12^2 + 39^2 = t^2$

    $144 + 1,521 = t^2$

    $1,665 = t^2$

    $\sqrt{1,665} = t$

    $40.8 \approx t$

    Add this length to the height of the bottom of the tree.

    $40.8 + 12 = 52.8$

    To the nearest tenth of a foot, the height of the tree was 52.8 ft.

## Focus on Higher Order Thinking

12. Let $p$ represent the length of the straight path across the park.

$$1.2^2 + 0.9^2 = p^2$$
$$1.44 + 0.81 = p^2$$
$$2.25 = p^2$$
$$1.5 \approx p$$

Multiply this distance by 2 to find the round trip distance.

$$2 \cdot 1.5 = 3$$

Using the path, the round trip distance is 3 miles. Joe usually walks $2(1.2 + 0.9) = 4.2$ miles, which is 1.2 miles further than taking the path across the park.

13. $\sqrt{x^2 + x^2}$ or $\sqrt{2x^2}$ or $x\sqrt{2}$ ; If $c$ represents the length of the hypotenuse, then $x^2 + x^2 = c^2$, and thus, $c = \sqrt{x^2 + x^2}$.

14. a. 0.57 in.; since the area of the square hamburger is 16 square inches, the length of each side is 4 inches. Let $d$ represent the distance from one corner of the hamburger to the opposite corner.

$$4^2 + 4^2 = d^2$$
$$16 + 16 = d^2$$
$$32 = d^2$$
$$\sqrt{32} = d$$
$$5.66 \approx d$$

The distance from the center of the hamburger to the corner is half of this length, or 2.83 inches. Since the area of the bun is 16 square inches, the radius of the bun is $\sqrt{\frac{16}{\pi}} \approx 2.26$ inches. Since $2.83 - 2.26 = 0.57$, each corner of the hamburger extends 0.57 inch beyond the bun.

b. The perpendicular distance from the center of the square to the any side is 2 inch. Subtract 2 inches from the radius of the bun.
$$2.26 - 2 = 0.26$$

The bun extends about 0.26 inches beyond the center of each side of the hamburger.

c. No; The burger sticks out a little more than one half inch, and the bun sticks out about a quarter inch, so the corners of the burger stick out more.

## LESSON 12.2

### Your Turn

2. Let $a = 14$, $b = 23$, $c = 25$.
$$14^2 + 23^2 \overset{?}{=} 25^2$$
$$196 + 529 \overset{?}{=} 625$$
$$725 \neq 625$$

The triangle is not a right triangle.

3. Let $a = 16$, $b = 30$, $c = 34$.
$$16^2 + 30^2 \overset{?}{=} 34^2$$
$$256 + 900 \overset{?}{=} 1,156$$
$$1,156 = 1,156$$

The triangle is a right triangle.

4. Let $a = 27$, $b = 36$, $c = 45$.
$$27^2 + 36^2 \overset{?}{=} 45^2$$
$$729 + 1,296 \overset{?}{=} 2,025$$
$$2,025 = 2,025$$

The triangle is a right triangle.

5. Let $a = 11$, $b = 18$, $c = 21$.
$$11^2 + 18^2 \overset{?}{=} 21^2$$
$$121 + 324 \overset{?}{=} 441$$
$$445 \neq 441$$

The triangle is not a right triangle.

6. Yes; Let $a = 480$, $b = 140$, $c = 500$. Then
$$a^2 + b^2 = 480^2 + 140^2$$
$$= 230,400 + 19,600$$
$$= 250,000$$

Since $c^2 = 500^2 = 250,000$, $a^2 + b^2 = c^2$.

Therefore, the playground is in the shape of a right triangle.

7. No; Let $a = 18$, $b = 19$, $c = 25$. Then
$$a^2 + b^2 = 18^2 + 19^2$$
$$= 324 + 361$$
$$= 685$$

Since $c^2 = 25^2 = 625$, $a^2 + b^2 \neq c^2$. Therefore, the piece of glass is not in the shape of a right triangle.

8. No; there are no pairs of whole numbers whose squares add to $12^2 = 144$.

### Guided Practice

1. a. 6 units, 8 units, 10 units

b. $6^2 + 8^2 \overset{?}{=} 10^2$
$$36 + 64 \overset{?}{=} 100$$
$$100 = 100$$

The triangle that Lashandra constructed is a right triangle.

2. Let $a = 9$, $b = 12$, and $c = 16$.
$$9^2 + 12^2 \overset{?}{=} 16^2$$
$$81 + 144 \overset{?}{=} 256$$
$$225 \neq 256$$

By the converse of the Pythagorean Theorem, the triangle is not a right triangle.

3. Yes; Let $a = 2.5$, $b = 6$, $c = 6.5$. Then

$$a^2 + b^2 = 2.5^2 + 6^2$$
$$= 6.25 + 36$$
$$= 42.25$$

Since $c^2 = 6.5^2 = 42.25$, $a^2 + b^2 = c^2$. Therefore, the triangle is a right triangle.

4. Test the side lengths in the equation $a^2 + b^2 = c^2$ using the longest side for $c$. If the equation is true, the triangle is a right triangle. Otherwise, it isn't.

## Independent Practice

5. Let $a = 11$, $b = 60$, $c = 61$.

$$11^2 + 60^2 \overset{?}{=} 61^2$$
$$121 + 3,600 \overset{?}{=} 3,721$$
$$3,721 = 3,721$$

The triangle is a right triangle.

6. Let $a = 5$, $b = 12$, $c = 15$.

$$5^2 + 12^2 \overset{?}{=} 15^2$$
$$25 + 144 \overset{?}{=} 225$$
$$169 \neq 225$$

The triangle is not a right triangle.

7. Let $a = 9$, $b = 15$, $c = 17$.

$$9^2 + 15^2 \overset{?}{=} 17^2$$
$$81 + 225 \overset{?}{=} 289$$
$$306 \neq 289$$

The triangle is not a right triangle.

8. Let $a = 15$, $b = 36$, $c = 39$.

$$15^2 + 36^2 \overset{?}{=} 39^2$$
$$225 + 1,296 \overset{?}{=} 1,521$$
$$1,521 = 1,521$$

The triangle is a right triangle.

9. Let $a = 20$, $b = 30$, $c = 40$.

$$20^2 + 30^2 \overset{?}{=} 40^2$$
$$400 + 900 \overset{?}{=} 1,600$$
$$1,300 \neq 1,600$$

The triangle is not a right triangle.

10. Let $a = 20$, $b = 48$, $c = 52$.

$$20^2 + 48^2 \overset{?}{=} 52^2$$
$$400 + 2,304 \overset{?}{=} 2,704$$
$$2,704 = 2,704$$

The triangle is a right triangle.

11. Let $a = 6$, $b = 17.5$, $c = 18.5$.

$$6^2 + 17.5^2 \overset{?}{=} 18.5^2$$
$$36 + 306.25 \overset{?}{=} 342.25$$
$$342.25 = 342.25$$

The triangle is a right triangle.

12. Let $a = 1.5$, $b = 2$, $c = 2.5$.

$$1.5^2 + 2^2 \overset{?}{=} 2.5^2$$
$$2.25 + 4 \overset{?}{=} 6.25$$
$$6.25 = 6.25$$

The triangle is a right triangle.

13. Let $a = 35$, $b = 45$, $c = 55$.

$$35^2 + 45^2 \overset{?}{=} 55^2$$
$$1,225 + 2,025 \overset{?}{=} 3,025$$
$$3,250 \neq 3,025$$

The triangle is not a right triangle.

14. Let $a = 14$, $b = 23$, $c = 25$.

$$14^2 + 23^2 \overset{?}{=} 25^2$$
$$196 + 529 \overset{?}{=} 625$$
$$725 \neq 625$$

The triangle is not a right triangle.

15. No; Let $a = 13$, $b = 14$, $c = 15$. Then

$$a^2 + b^2 = 13^2 + 14^2$$
$$= 169 + 196$$
$$= 365$$

Since $c^2 = 15^2 = 225$, $a^2 + b^2 \neq c^2$. Therefore, the triangle is not a right triangle.

16. Yes; Let $a = 4.8$, $b = 6.4$, $c = 8$. Then

$$a^2 + b^2 = 4.8^2 + 6.4^2$$
$$= 23.04 + 40.96$$
$$= 64$$

Since $c^2 = 8^2 = 64$, $a^2 + b^2 = c^2$. Therefore, the fabric is in the shape of a right triangle.

17. No; Let $a = 6$, $b = 10$, $c = 12$. Then

$$a^2 + b^2 = 6^2 + 10^2$$
$$= 36 + 100$$
$$= 136$$

Since $c^2 = 12^2 = 144$, $a^2 + b^2 \neq c^2$. Therefore, the tiles are not in the shape of a right triangle.

18. Sample answer: The knots are evenly spaced, so the side lengths are 3 units, 4 units, and 5 units. Since $3^2 + 4^2 = 5^2$, the sides form a right triangle.

19. Yes; Since $0.75^2 + 1^2 = 1.25^2$, the triangles are right triangles. Adjoining them at their hypotenuses will form a rectangle with sides 1 m and 0.75 m.

20. No; She did not use the longest length for $c$. $8^2 + 15^2 = 17^2$, so it is a right triangle.

## Focus on Higher Order Thinking

21. Yes. His conjecture is true; Students' work will vary but should show that they've used the converse of the Pythagorean Theorem to test whether the new triangles are right triangles.

22. Yes; 1 ft = 12 in. Since $12^2 + 35^2 = 37^2$, each half of the parallelogram is a right triangle. Therefore, the sides of the parallelogram meet at right angles, making the parallelogram a rectangle.

23. Sample answer: She could measure the diagonal of the field to see if the sides of the field and the diagonal form a right triangle. Since $48^2 + 90^2 = 10{,}404$, and $\sqrt{10{,}404} = 102$, the diagonal should measure 102 yards if the sides of the field meet at right angles.

## LESSON 12.3

### Your Turn

1. The legs measure 4 units and 5 units. Let $a = 4$ and $b = 5$.

$$a^2 + b^2 = c^2$$
$$4^2 + 5^2 = c^2$$
$$16 + 25 = c^2$$
$$41 = c^2$$
$$\sqrt{41} = c$$

Since $\sqrt{41}$ is between $\sqrt{36}$ and $\sqrt{49}$, it is between 6 and 7. Since 41 is about halfway between 36 and 49, $\sqrt{41} \approx 6.4$. The hypotenuse is about 6.4 units long.

4. The length of the horizontal leg is the absolute value of the difference between the $x$-coordinates of the points $(10, 20)$ and $(200, 20)$, which is 190. The length of the vertical leg is the absolute value of the difference between the $y$-coordinates of the points $(200, 120)$ and $(200, 20)$, which is 100.

$$a^2 + b^2 = c^2$$
$$190^2 + 100^2 = c^2$$
$$36{,}100 + 10{,}000 = c^2$$
$$46{,}100 = c^2$$
$$\sqrt{46{,}100} = c$$
$$214.7 \approx c$$

The distance is approximately 214.7 meters.

### Guided Practice

1. The legs measure 3 units and 5 units. Let $a = 3$ and $b = 5$.

$$a^2 + b^2 = c^2$$
$$3^2 + 5^2 = c^2$$
$$9 + 25 = c^2$$
$$34 = c^2$$
$$\sqrt{34} = c$$

Since $\sqrt{34}$ is between $\sqrt{25}$ and $\sqrt{36}$, it is between 5 and 6. Since 34 is closer to 36, $\sqrt{34} \approx 5.8$. The hypotenuse is about 5.8 units long.

2. Let $(x_1, y_1) = (3, 7)$ and $(x_2, y_2) = (15, 12)$.

$$d = \sqrt{(x_2 - x_1)^2 + (y_2 - y_1)^2}$$
$$d = \sqrt{(15 - 3)^2 + (12 - 7)^2}$$
$$d = \sqrt{12^2 + 5^2}$$
$$d = \sqrt{144 + 25}$$
$$d = \sqrt{169}$$
$$d = 13$$

The distance is 13 units.

3. The distance between the airport and the plane at $(1, 80)$ is 79 miles. The distance between the airport and the plane at $(68, 1)$ is 67 miles.

$$a^2 + b^2 = c^2$$
$$79^2 + 67^2 = c^2$$
$$6{,}241 + 4{,}489 = c^2$$
$$10{,}730 = c^2$$
$$\sqrt{10{,}730} = c$$
$$103.6 \approx c$$

The distance between the two planes is approximately 103.6 miles.

4. Sample answer: Draw a right triangle whose hypotenuse is the segment connecting the two points and then use the Pythagorean Theorem to find the length of that segment, or use the Distance Formula.

### Independent Practice

5. The legs measure 6 units and 5 units. Let $a = 6$ and $b = 5$.

$$a^2 + b^2 = c^2$$
$$6^2 + 5^2 = c^2$$
$$36 + 25 = c^2$$
$$61 = c^2$$
$$\sqrt{61} = c$$

Since $\sqrt{61}$ is between $\sqrt{49}$ and $\sqrt{64}$, it is between 7 and 8. Since $\sqrt{56}$ is about half way between the two, the distance is greater than 7.5. 61 is much closer to 64, so the length of the longest side is between 7.5 in. and 7.8 in.

6. Let $(x_1, y_1) = (17, 21)$ and $(x_2, y_2) = (28, 13)$.

$$d = \sqrt{(x_2 - x_1)^2 + (y_2 - y_1)^2}$$
$$d = \sqrt{(28 - 17)^2 + (13 - 21)^2}$$
$$d = \sqrt{11^2 + (-8)^2}$$
$$d = \sqrt{121 + 64}$$
$$d = \sqrt{185}$$
$$d \approx 13.6$$

The distance is approximately 13.6 miles.

7.

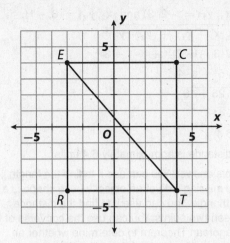

a. The legs of each triangle measure 7 units and 8 units. Let $a = 7$ and $b = 8$.

$$a^2 + b^2 = c^2$$
$$7^2 + 8^2 = c^2$$
$$49 + 64 = c^2$$
$$113 = c^2$$
$$\sqrt{113} = c$$
$$ET = \sqrt{113} \text{ units}$$

b. Let $(x_1, y_1) = (-3, 4)$ and $(x_2, y_2) = (4, -4)$.

$$d = \sqrt{(x_2 - x_1)^2 + (y_2 - y_1)^2}$$
$$d = \sqrt{(4 - (-3))^2 + (-4 - 4)^2}$$
$$d = \sqrt{7^2 + (-8)^2}$$
$$d = \sqrt{49 + 64}$$
$$d = \sqrt{113}$$

8. Plot the three points. Draw each distance as the hypotenuse of a right triangle. From the graph it appears that the ships at points $P$ and $Q$ are farthest apart. The Pythagorean Theorem or Distance Formula can be used to verify that this is the case.

$(PQ = \sqrt{125}$ units, $QR = \sqrt{85}$ units, and $PR = \sqrt{80}$ units)

9. The following points are all 5 units from the origin: $(5, 0)$, $(4, 3)$, $(3, 4)$, $(0, 5)$, $(-3, 4)$, $(-4, 3)$, $(-5, 0)$, $(-4, -3)$, $(-3, -4)$, $(0, -5)$, $(3, -4)$, $(4, -3)$; the points would form a circle.

10. Let $(x_1, y_1) = (0, 25)$ and $(x_2, y_2) = (30, 10)$.

$$d = \sqrt{(x_2 - x_1)^2 + (y_2 - y_1)^2}$$
$$d = \sqrt{(30 - 0)^2 + (10 - 25)^2}$$
$$d = \sqrt{30^2 + (-15)^2}$$
$$d = \sqrt{900 + 225}$$
$$d = \sqrt{1125}$$
$$d \approx 33.5$$

Yes; The distance from the motion detector to the peacock is approximately 33.5 ft, which is less than 34 ft.

## Focus on Higher Order Thinking

11.

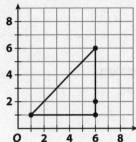

Let $(x_1, y_1) = (6, 6)$ and $(x_2, y_2) = (1, 1)$.

$$d = \sqrt{(x_2 - x_1)^2 + (y_2 - y_1)^2}$$
$$d = \sqrt{(6 - 1)^2 + (6 - 1)^2}$$
$$d = \sqrt{5^2 + 5^2}$$
$$d = \sqrt{25 + 25}$$
$$d = \sqrt{50}$$
$$d \approx 7.1$$

The length of the hypotenuse is approximately 7.1 units.

12. Create a right triangle with hypotenuse $\overline{AB}$. The vertex at the right angle is either $(40, 14)$ or $(75, 26)$. The lengths of the legs of the triangle are 12 yards and 35 yards. Let $a = 12$ and $b = 35$.

$$a^2 + b^2 = c^2$$
$$12^2 + 35^2 = c^2$$
$$144 + 1{,}225 = c^2$$
$$1{,}369 = c^2$$
$$37 = c$$

The distance between $A$ and $B$ is 37 yards.

## MODULE 12

### Ready to Go On?

1. $a^2 + b^2 = c^2$
$$a^2 + 21^2 = 35^2$$
$$a^2 + 441 = 1{,}225$$
$$a^2 = 784$$
$$a = 28$$

The length of the leg is 28 m.

2. $a^2 + b^2 = c^2$
$$16^2 + 30^2 = c^2$$
$$256 + 900 = c^2$$
$$1{,}156 = c^2$$
$$34 = c$$

The length of the hypotenuse is 34 ft.

3. Let $a = 11$, $b = 60$, $c = 61$.

$11^2 + 60^2 \overset{?}{=} 61^2$

$121 + 3{,}600 \overset{?}{=} 3{,}721$

$3{,}721 = 3{,}721$

The triangle is a right triangle.

4. Let $a = 9$, $b = 37$, $c = 40$.

$9^2 + 37^2 \overset{?}{=} 40^2$

$81 + 1{,}369 \overset{?}{=} 1{,}600$

$1{,}450 \neq 1{,}600$

The triangle is not a right triangle.

5. Let $a = 15$, $b = 35$, $c = 38$.

$15^2 + 35^2 \overset{?}{=} 38^2$

$225 + 1{,}225 \overset{?}{=} 1{,}444$

$1{,}450 \neq 1{,}444$

The triangle is not a right triangle.

6. Let $a = 28$, $b = 45$, $c = 53$.

$28^2 + 45^2 \overset{?}{=} 53^2$

$784 + 2{,}025 \overset{?}{=} 2{,}809$

$2{,}809 = 2{,}809$

The triangle is a right triangle.

7. Let $a = 4.5$, $b = 6$, $c = 7.5$.

$4.5^2 + 6^2 \overset{?}{=} 7.5^2$

$20.25 + 36 \overset{?}{=} 56.25$

$56.25 = 56.25$

Yes; The card is a right triangle.

8. Let $(x_1, y_1) = (-2, 3)$ and $(x_2, y_2) = (4, 6)$.

$d = \sqrt{(x_2 - x_1)^2 + (y_2 - y_1)^2}$

$d = \sqrt{(4 - (-2))^2 + (6 - 3)^2}$

$d = \sqrt{6^2 + 3^2}$

$d = \sqrt{36 + 9}$

$d = \sqrt{45}$

$d \approx 6.7$

The distance is approximately 6.7 units.

9. Let $(x_1, y_1) = (4, 6)$ and $(x_2, y_2) = (3, -1)$.

$d = \sqrt{(x_2 - x_1)^2 + (y_2 - y_1)^2}$

$d = \sqrt{(3 - 4)^2 + (-1 - 6)^2}$

$d = \sqrt{(-1)^2 + (-7)^2}$

$d = \sqrt{1 + 49}$

$d = \sqrt{50}$

$d \approx 7.1$

The distance is approximately 7.1 units.

10. Let $(x_1, y_1) = (-2, 3)$ and $(x_2, y_2) = (3, -1)$.

$d = \sqrt{(x_2 - x_1)^2 + (y_2 - y_1)^2}$

$d = \sqrt{(3 - (-2))^2 + (-1 - 3)^2}$

$d = \sqrt{5^2 + (-4)^2}$

$d = \sqrt{25 + 16}$

$d = \sqrt{41}$

$d \approx 6.4$

The distance is approximately 6.4 units.

11. Sample answer: You can use it to find the length of the missing side of an object whose shape is a right triangle. You can use it to find the distance between two points. You can use the converse of the Pythagorean Theorem to determine whether an object is in the shape of a right triangle.

## MODULE 13 *Volume*

### Are You Ready?

1. $11^2 = 11 \times 11 = 121$

2. $2^5 = 2 \times 2 \times 2 \times 2 \times 2 = 32$

3. $\left(\frac{1}{5}\right)^3 = \left(\frac{1}{5}\right) \times \left(\frac{1}{5}\right) \times \left(\frac{1}{5}\right) = \frac{1}{125}$

4. $(0.3)^2 = (0.3) \times (0.3) = 0.09$

5. $2.1^3 = 2.1 \times 2.1 \times 2.1 = 9.261$

6. $0.1^3 = 0.1 \times 0.1 \times 0.1 = 0.001$

7. $\left(\frac{9.6}{3}\right)^2 = \frac{9.6}{3} \times \frac{9.6}{3}$

$\phantom{7.}\quad = \frac{92.16}{9} = 10.24$

8. $100^3 = 100 \times 100 \times 100$
$\phantom{8.}\;\; 1,000,000$

9. $2.3\underline{7}4 \rightarrow 2.37$

10. $126.\underline{3}99 \rightarrow 126$

11. $13.\underline{9}577 \rightarrow 14.0$

12. $42.6\underline{9}0 \rightarrow 42.69$

13. $134.\underline{9}5 \rightarrow 135.0$

14. $2.\underline{0}486 \rightarrow 2.0$

15. $63.6\underline{3}52 \rightarrow 63.64$

16. $98.\underline{9}499 \rightarrow 98.9$

17. $3.14(5)^2(10)$
$\phantom{17.}\;3.14(25)(10)$
$\phantom{17.}\;78.5(10)$
$\phantom{17.}\;785$

18. $\frac{1}{3}(3.14)(3)^2(5)$

$\phantom{18.}\;\frac{1}{3}(3.14)(9)(5)$

$\phantom{18.}\;\frac{1}{{}_1\cancel{3}}(3.14)(\cancel{9}^3)(5)$

$\phantom{18.}\;3.14(3)(5)$
$\phantom{18.}\;9.42(5)$
$\phantom{18.}\;47.1$

19. $\frac{4}{3}(3.14)(3)^3$

$\phantom{19.}\;\frac{4}{3}(3.14)(27)$

$\phantom{19.}\;\frac{4}{{}_1\cancel{3}}(3.14)(\cancel{27}^9)$

$\phantom{19.}\;4(3.14)(9)$
$\phantom{19.}\;12.56(9)$
$\phantom{19.}\;113.04$

20. $\frac{4}{3}(3.14)(6)^3$

$\phantom{20.}\;\frac{4}{3}(3.14)(216)$

$\phantom{20.}\;\frac{4}{{}_1\cancel{3}}(3.14)(\cancel{216}^{72})$

$\phantom{20.}\;4(3.14)(72)$
$\phantom{20.}\;12.56(72)$
$\phantom{20.}\;904.32$

21. $3.14(4)^2(9)$
$\phantom{21.}\;3.14(16)(9)$
$\phantom{21.}\;50.24(9)$
$\phantom{21.}\;452.16$

22. $\frac{1}{3}(3.14)(9)^2\left(\frac{2}{3}\right)$

$\phantom{22.}\;\frac{1}{3}(3.14)(81)\left(\frac{2}{3}\right)$

$\phantom{22.}\;\frac{1}{{}_1\cancel{3}}(3.14)(\cancel{81}^{27})\left(\frac{2}{3}\right)$

$\phantom{22.}\;1(3.14)(\cancel{27}^9)\left(\frac{2}{\cancel{3}}\right)$

$\phantom{22.}\;3.14(9)(2)$
$\phantom{22.}\;28.26(2)$
$\phantom{22.}\;56.52$

### LESSON 13.1

#### Your Turn

4. Since the diameter is 10 in., the radius is 5 in.
The height is 6 in.
$V = \pi r^2 h$
$\phantom{V}\approx 3.14 \cdot 5^2 \cdot 6$
$\phantom{V}\approx 3.14 \cdot 25 \cdot 6$
$\phantom{V}\approx 471$
The volume is approximately 471 in$^3$.

5. The radius is 4 ft. The height is 12 ft.
$V = \pi r^2 h$
$\phantom{V}\approx 3.14 \cdot 4^2 \cdot 12$
$\phantom{V}\approx 3.14 \cdot 16 \cdot 12$
$\phantom{V}\approx 602.9$
The volume is approximately 602.9 ft$^3$.

6. Since the diameter is 12 in., the radius is 6 in.
The height is 4 in.
$V = \pi r^2 h$
$\phantom{V}\approx 3.14 \cdot 6^2 \cdot 4$
$\phantom{V}\approx 3.14 \cdot 36 \cdot 4$
$\phantom{V}\approx 452.2$
The volume is approximately 452.2 in$^3$.

#### Guided Practice

1. The bases are two congruent circles that lie in parallel planes.

2. Sample answer: 427 in$^3$; there are 61 cubes on the bottom of the cylinder. The height is 7 cubes.
$V = Bh \approx 61 \cdot 7$ or 427 in$^3$.

3. The radius is 6 m. The height is 15 m.
$$V = \pi r^2 h$$
$$\approx 3.14 \cdot 6^2 \cdot 15$$
$$\approx 3.14 \cdot 36 \cdot 15$$
$$\approx 1{,}695.6$$
The volume of the cylinder is approximately 1,695.6 m³.

4. Since the diameter measures about 2.7 m, the radius measures about 1.35 m. The height measures about 2.7 m.
$$V = \pi r^2 h$$
$$\approx 3.14 \cdot 1.35^2 \cdot 2.7$$
$$\approx 3.14 \cdot 1.8225 \cdot 2.7$$
$$\approx 15.5$$
The radius of the drum is about 1.35 m.
The volume of the drum is about 15.5 m³.

5. You need to know the height and know or be able to calculate the radius of the base. Then you can substitute into the volume formula, $V = \pi r^2 h$.

## Independent Practice

6. The radius is 11 cm. The height is 1.5 cm.
$$V = \pi r^2 h$$
$$\approx 3.14 \cdot 11^2 \cdot 1.5$$
$$\approx 3.14 \cdot 121 \cdot 1.5$$
$$\approx 569.9$$
The volume is approximately 569.9 cm³.

7. The radius is 4 in. The height is 24 in.
$$V = \pi r^2 h$$
$$\approx 3.14 \cdot 4^2 \cdot 24$$
$$\approx 3.14 \cdot 16 \cdot 24$$
$$\approx 1{,}205.8$$
The volume is approximately 1,205.8 in³.

8. The radius is 5 m. The height is 16 m.
$$V = \pi r^2 h$$
$$\approx 3.14 \cdot 5^2 \cdot 16$$
$$\approx 3.14 \cdot 25 \cdot 16$$
$$\approx 1{,}256$$
The volume is approximately 1,256 m³.

9. Since the diameter is 10 in., the radius is 5 in. The height is 12 in.
$$V = \pi r^2 h$$
$$\approx 3.14 \cdot 5^2 \cdot 12$$
$$\approx 3.14 \cdot 25 \cdot 12$$
$$\approx 942$$
The volume is approximately 942 in³.

10. $r = 4$ cm, $h = 40$ cm
$$V = \pi r^2 h$$
$$\approx 3.14 \cdot 4^2 \cdot 40$$
$$\approx 3.14 \cdot 16 \cdot 40$$
$$\approx 2{,}009.6$$
The volume is approximately 2,009.6 cm³.

11. $r = 8$ m, $h = 4$ m
$$V = \pi r^2 h$$
$$\approx 3.14 \cdot 8^2 \cdot 4$$
$$\approx 3.14 \cdot 64 \cdot 4$$
$$\approx 803.8$$
The volume is approximately 803.8 m³.

12. $r = 18.8$ ft, $h = 24$ ft
$$V = \pi r^2 h$$
$$\approx 3.14 \cdot 18.8^2 \cdot 24$$
$$\approx 3.14 \cdot 353.44 \cdot 24$$
$$\approx 26{,}635.2$$
The volume is approximately 26,635.2 ft³.

13. Since $d = 22$ in., $r = 11$ in., $h = 18$ in.
$$V = \pi r^2 h$$
$$\approx 3.14 \cdot 11^2 \cdot 18$$
$$\approx 3.14 \cdot 121 \cdot 18$$
$$\approx 6{,}838.9$$
The volume is approximately 6,838.9 in³.

14. Since $d = 11.1$ ft, $r = 5.55$ ft, $h = 20$ ft.
$$V = \pi r^2 h$$
$$\approx 3.14 \cdot 5.55^2 \cdot 20$$
$$\approx 3.14 \cdot 30.8025 \cdot 20$$
$$\approx 1{,}934.4$$
The volume is approximately 1,934.4 ft³.

15. Since $d = 120$ m, $r = 60$ m, $h = 30$ m.
$$V = \pi r^2 h$$
$$\approx 3.14 \cdot 60^2 \cdot 30$$
$$\approx 3.14 \cdot 3{,}600 \cdot 30$$
$$\approx 339{,}120$$
The volume is approximately 339,120 m³.

16. Since $d = 6$ in., $r = 3$ in., which is 0.25 ft. $h = 5{,}280$ ft.
$$V = \pi r^2 h$$
$$\approx 3.14 \cdot 0.25^2 \cdot 5{,}280$$
$$\approx 3.14 \cdot 0.0625 \cdot 5{,}280$$
$$\approx 1{,}036.2$$

The volume of oil contained in 1 mile of pipeline is approximately 1,036.2 ft³. Divide by 5.61.

$$1{,}036.2 \div 5.61 \approx 184.7$$

One mile of pipeline contains about 184.7 barrels of oil. At $100 per barrel, this oil is worth 184.7 · $100, or $18,470.

17. Since $d = 3.5$ in., $r = 1.75$ in., $h = 12$ in.
$$V = \pi r^2 h$$
$$\approx 3.14 \cdot 1.75^2 \cdot 12$$
$$\approx 3.14 \cdot 3.0625 \cdot 12$$
$$\approx 115.395$$

Divide by 2.
$$115.395 \div 2 = 57.6975$$
The volume is approximately 57.7 in³.

## Focus on Higher Order Thinking

18. Sample answer: The volumes are equal because a cylinder with a 3-inch diameter has a 1.5-inch radius.

19. Divide the diameter by 2 to find the radius. Then substitute the volume and radius in $V = \pi r^2 h$ and solve for $h$. Sample example: For a cylinder with volume 72 m³ and a diameter of 6 m,

$$72 = \pi \cdot 3^2 \cdot h, \text{ so } h = \frac{72}{9\pi} = \frac{8}{\pi} \approx 2.5 \text{ m.}$$

20. $\frac{1}{4}$; for any height $h$, cylinder A has a volume of $36\pi \cdot h$. Cylinder B has a volume of $9\pi \cdot h$. Since 9 is $\frac{1}{4}$ of 36, the volume of cylinder B is $\frac{1}{4}$ the volume of cylinder A.

## LESSON 13.2

### Your Turn

4. Since the diameter is 15 cm, the radius is 7.5 cm. The height is 16 cm.
$$V = \frac{1}{3}\pi r^2 h$$
$$\approx \frac{1}{3} \cdot 3.14 \cdot 7.5^2 \cdot 16$$
$$\approx \frac{1}{3} \cdot 3.14 \cdot 56.25 \cdot 16$$
$$\approx 942$$
The volume is approximately 942 cm$^3$.

5. The radius is 2 ft. The height is 3 ft.
$$V = \frac{1}{3}\pi r^2 h$$
$$\approx \frac{1}{3} \cdot 3.14 \cdot 2^2 \cdot 3$$
$$\approx \frac{1}{3} \cdot 3.14 \cdot 4 \cdot 3$$
$$\approx 12.6$$
The volume is approximately 12.6 ft$^3$.

6. Since $d = 424$ m, $r = 212$ m, $h = 410$ m.
$$V = \frac{1}{3}\pi r^2 h$$
$$\approx \frac{1}{3} \cdot 3.14 \cdot 212^2 \cdot 410$$
$$\approx \frac{1}{3} \cdot 3.14 \cdot 44{,}944 \cdot 410$$
$$\approx 19{,}286{,}968.5$$
The volume is approximately 19,286,968.5 m$^3$.

### Guided Practice

1. $V_{\text{cylinder}} = Bh = 45 \cdot 10 = 450$

$V_{\text{cone}} = \frac{1}{3}V_{\text{cylinder}}$

$= \frac{1}{3} \cdot 450$

$= 150$

The volume of the cone is 150 in$^3$.

2. 54 m$^3$; the volume of a cylinder is 3 times the volume of a cone that has the same base and height.

3. Since $d = 6$ ft, $r = 3$ ft, $h = 7$ ft
$$V = \frac{1}{3}\pi r^2 h$$
$$\approx \frac{1}{3} \cdot 3.14 \cdot 3^2 \cdot 7$$
$$\approx \frac{1}{3} \cdot 3.14 \cdot 9 \cdot 7$$
$$\approx 65.9$$
The volume is approximately 65.9 ft$^3$.

4. $r = 33$ in., $h = 100$ in.
$$V = \frac{1}{3}\pi r^2 h$$
$$\approx \frac{1}{3} \cdot 3.14 \cdot 33^2 \cdot 100$$
$$\approx \frac{1}{3} \cdot 3.14 \cdot 1{,}089 \cdot 100$$
$$\approx 113{,}982$$
The volume is approximately 113,982 in$^3$.

5. $r = 3$ in., $h = 15$ in.
$$V = \frac{1}{3}\pi r^2 h$$
$$\approx \frac{1}{3} \cdot 3.14 \cdot 3^2 \cdot 15$$
$$\approx \frac{1}{3} \cdot 3.14 \cdot 9 \cdot 15$$
$$\approx 141.3$$
The volume is approximately 141.3 in$^3$.

6. Since $d = 50$ m, $r = 25$ m, $h = 20$ m.
$$V = \frac{1}{3}\pi r^2 h$$
$$\approx \frac{1}{3} \cdot 3.14 \cdot 25^2 \cdot 20$$
$$\approx \frac{1}{3} \cdot 3.14 \cdot 625 \cdot 20$$
$$\approx 13{,}083.3$$
The volume is approximately 13,083.3 m$^3$.

7. You can find $\frac{1}{3}$ of the volume of a cylinder with the same base and height, or you can use the formula $V = \frac{1}{3}\pi r^2 h$.

### Independent Practice

8. $r = 7$ mm, $h = 8$ mm
$$V = \frac{1}{3}\pi r^2 h$$
$$\approx \frac{1}{3} \cdot 3.14 \cdot 7^2 \cdot 8$$
$$\approx \frac{1}{3} \cdot 3.14 \cdot 49 \cdot 8$$
$$\approx 410.3$$
The volume is approximately 410.3 mm$^3$.

9. $r = 2$ in., $h = 6$ in.
$$V = \frac{1}{3}\pi r^2 h$$
$$\approx \frac{1}{3} \cdot 3.14 \cdot 2^2 \cdot 6$$
$$\approx \frac{1}{3} \cdot 3.14 \cdot 4 \cdot 6$$
$$\approx 25.1$$
The volume is approximately 25.1 in$^3$.

10. Since $d = 6$ cm, $r = 3$ cm, $h = 11.5$ cm.
$$V = \frac{1}{3}\pi r^2 h$$
$$\approx \frac{1}{3} \cdot 3.14 \cdot 3^2 \cdot 11.5$$
$$\approx \frac{1}{3} \cdot 3.14 \cdot 9 \cdot 11.5$$
$$\approx 108.3$$
The volume is approximately 108.3 cm$^3$.

11. $r = 3$ m, $h = 10$ m

$$V = \frac{1}{3}\pi r^2 h$$

$$\approx \frac{1}{3} \cdot 3.14 \cdot 3^2 \cdot 10$$

$$\approx \frac{1}{3} \cdot 3.14 \cdot 9 \cdot 10$$

$$\approx 94.2$$

The volume is approximately 94.2 m³.

12. $r = 0.75$ in., $h = 3$ in.

$$V = \frac{1}{3}\pi r^2 h$$

$$\approx \frac{1}{3} \cdot 3.14 \cdot 0.75^2 \cdot 3$$

$$\approx \frac{1}{3} \cdot 3.14 \cdot 0.5625 \cdot 3$$

$$\approx 1.8$$

The volume is approximately 1.8 in³.

13. Since $d = 8$ in., $r = 4$ in., $h = 10$ in.

$$V = \frac{1}{3}\pi r^2 h$$

$$\approx \frac{1}{3} \cdot 3.14 \cdot 4^2 \cdot 10$$

$$\approx \frac{1}{3} \cdot 3.14 \cdot 16 \cdot 10$$

$$\approx 167.5$$

The container holds approximately 167.5 in³.

14. Since $d = 300$ m, $r = 150$ m, $h = 150$ m.

$$V = \frac{1}{3}\pi r^2 h$$

$$\approx \frac{1}{3} \cdot 3.14 \cdot 150^2 \cdot 150$$

$$\approx \frac{1}{3} \cdot 3.14 \cdot 22,500 \cdot 150$$

$$\approx 3,532,500$$

The volume is approximately 3,532,500 m³.

15. Since $d = 10$ in., $r = 5$ in. The height is 2 feet, which is 24 inches, so $h = 24$ in.

$$V = \frac{1}{3}\pi r^2 h$$

$$\approx \frac{1}{3} \cdot 3.14 \cdot 5^2 \cdot 24$$

$$\approx \frac{1}{3} \cdot 3.14 \cdot 25 \cdot 24$$

$$\approx 628$$

The volume is approximately 628 in³.

16.

$$V = \frac{1}{3}\pi r^2 h$$

$$100.48 = \frac{1}{3}\pi r^2 \cdot 6$$

$$100.48 = 2\pi r^2$$

$$\frac{100.48}{2\pi} = r^2$$

$$16 \approx r^2$$

$$4 \approx r$$

The radius is approximately 4 in.

17.

$$V = \frac{1}{3}\pi r^2 h$$

$$56.52 = \frac{1}{3}\pi \cdot 3^2 \cdot h$$

$$56.52 = 3\pi h$$

$$\frac{56.52}{3\pi} = h$$

$$6 \approx h$$

The height is approximately 6 cm.

18. Since $d = 4$ in., $r = 2$ in., $h = 6$ in.

$$V = \frac{1}{3}\pi r^2 h$$

$$\approx \frac{1}{3} \cdot 3.14 \cdot 2^2 \cdot 6$$

$$\approx \frac{1}{3} \cdot 3.14 \cdot 4 \cdot 6$$

$$\approx 25.12$$

The volume of the cone is approximately 25.12 in³. The volume of the cylinder is 3 times this measurement, or 75.36 in³. Subtract to find the difference: $75.36 - 25.12 = 50.24$ in³.

**Focus on Higher Order Thinking**

19. a. He needs to know either the diameter or the radius of the base.

b. No; The radius of each layer of sand decreases from bottom to top. Therefore, as the volume of sand increases, the height increases at a faster rate.

20.

$$V = \frac{1}{3}\pi r^2 h$$

$$301.44 = \frac{1}{3}\pi r^2 \cdot 18$$

$$301.44 = 6\pi r^2$$

$$\frac{301.44}{6\pi} = r^2$$

$$16 \approx r^2$$

$$4 \approx r$$

The radius is approximately 4 cm. Therefore, the diameter is approximately 8 cm, and $x \approx 8$.

21. Since the radius and the height of the cone and the cylinder are the same, the volume of the cylinder is 3 times the volume of the cone. Therefore, it will take 3 cones of liquid to fill the cylinder.

22. No; The volume of the cone will be 3 times that of the cylinder because the radius is squared in the formula. For example, for a cylinder with radius 1 and height 5, $V = \pi \cdot 1^2 \cdot 5 = 5\pi$. For a cone with radius 3 and height 5, $V = \frac{1}{3} \cdot \pi \cdot 3^2 \cdot 5 = 15\pi$, which is 3 times the volume of the cylinder.

## LESSON 13.3

### Your Turn

2. $V = \frac{4}{3}\pi r^3$

$\approx \frac{4}{3} \cdot 3.14 \cdot 10^3$

$\approx \frac{4}{3} \cdot 3.14 \cdot 1000$

$\approx 4,186.7$

The volume is approximately 4,186.7 cm³.

3. Since $d = 3.4$ m, $r = 1.7$ m.

$V = \frac{4}{3}\pi r^3$

$\approx \frac{4}{3} \cdot 3.14 \cdot 1.7^3$

$\approx \frac{4}{3} \cdot 3.14 \cdot 4.913$

$\approx 20.6$

The volume is approximately 20.6 m³.

6. Since $d = 12$ in., $r = 6$ in.

$V = \frac{4}{3}\pi r^3$

$\approx \frac{4}{3} \cdot 3.14 \cdot 6^3$

$\approx \frac{4}{3} \cdot 3.14 \cdot 216$

$\approx 904.3$

The volume is approximately 904.3 in³.

### Guided Practice

1. A sphere is a three-dimensional figure with all points the same distance from the center.

2. The radius is the distance from the center of a sphere to a point on the sphere.

3. $V = \frac{4}{3}\pi r^3$

$\approx \frac{4}{3} \cdot 3.14 \cdot 1^3$

$\approx \frac{4}{3} \cdot 3.14 \cdot 1$

$\approx 4.2$

The volume is approximately 4.2 in³.

4. Since $d = 20$ cm, $r = 10$ cm.

$V = \frac{4}{3}\pi r^3$

$\approx \frac{4}{3} \cdot 3.14 \cdot 10^3$

$\approx \frac{4}{3} \cdot 3.14 \cdot 1,000$

$\approx 4,186.7$

The volume is approximately 4,186.7 cm³.

5. $V = \frac{4}{3}\pi r^3$

$\approx \frac{4}{3} \cdot 3.14 \cdot 1.5^3$

$\approx \frac{4}{3} \cdot 3.14 \cdot 3.375$

$\approx 14.1$

The volume is approximately 14.1 ft³.

6. Since $d = 2$ yd, $r = 1$ yd.

$V = \frac{4}{3}\pi r^3$

$\approx \frac{4}{3} \cdot 3.14 \cdot 1^3$

$\approx \frac{4}{3} \cdot 3.14 \cdot 1$

$\approx 4.2$

The volume is approximately 4.2 yd³.

7. Since $d = 2.9$ in., $r = 1.45$ in.

$V = \frac{4}{3}\pi r^3$

$\approx \frac{4}{3} \cdot 3.14 \cdot 1.45^3$

$\approx \frac{4}{3} \cdot 3.14 \cdot 3.048625$

$\approx 12.8$

The volume is approximately 12.8 in³.

8. Since the circumference is 29.5 in., and $C = 2\pi r$,

$r = \frac{29.5}{2\pi} \approx 4.7$ in.

$V = \frac{4}{3}\pi r^3$

$\approx \frac{4}{3} \cdot 3.14 \cdot 4.7^3$

$\approx \frac{4}{3} \cdot 3.14 \cdot 103.823$

$\approx 434.7$

The volume is approximately 435 in³.

9. a. $\frac{1}{3}$; the ball takes up $\frac{2}{3}$ of the space, so $\frac{1}{3}$ is empty.

   b. Each side of the box measures $2r$ units. The volume is $(2r)^3$, or $8r^3$ cubic units.

   c. Almost $\frac{1}{2}$ the box is empty. The amount of empty space is $8r^3 - \frac{4}{3}\pi r^3 \approx 3.81r^3$ cubic units, and $\frac{3.81}{8} \approx 0.48$.

10. Find the radius. Then substitute for $r$ in the formula $V = \frac{4}{3}\pi r^3$ and simplify.

### Independent Practice

11. $V = \frac{4}{3}\pi r^3$

$\approx \frac{4}{3} \cdot 3.14 \cdot 3.1^3$

$\approx \frac{4}{3} \cdot 3.14 \cdot 29.791$

$\approx 124.7$

The volume is approximately 124.7 m³.

12. Since $d = 18$ in., $r = 9$ in.

$$V = \frac{4}{3}\pi r^3$$

$$\approx \frac{4}{3} \cdot 3.14 \cdot 9^3$$

$$\approx \frac{4}{3} \cdot 3.14 \cdot 729$$

$$\approx 3{,}052.1$$

The volume is approximately 3,052.1 in³.

13. $V = \frac{4}{3}\pi r^3$

$$\approx \frac{4}{3} \cdot 3.14 \cdot 6^3$$

$$\approx \frac{4}{3} \cdot 3.14 \cdot 216$$

$$\approx 904.3$$

The volume is approximately 904.3 in³.

14. Since $d = 36$ m, $r = 18$ m.

$$V = \frac{4}{3}\pi r^3$$

$$\approx \frac{4}{3} \cdot 3.14 \cdot 18^3$$

$$\approx \frac{4}{3} \cdot 3.14 \cdot 5{,}832$$

$$\approx 24{,}416.6$$

The volume is approximately 24,416.6 m³.

15. $V = \frac{4}{3}\pi r^3$

$$\approx \frac{4}{3} \cdot 3.14 \cdot 11^3$$

$$\approx \frac{4}{3} \cdot 3.14 \cdot 1{,}331$$

$$\approx 5{,}572.5$$

The volume is approximately 5,572.5 cm³.

16. Since $d = 2.5$ ft, $r = 1.25$ ft.

$$V = \frac{4}{3}\pi r^3$$

$$\approx \frac{4}{3} \cdot 3.14 \cdot 1.25^3$$

$$\approx \frac{4}{3} \cdot 3.14 \cdot 1.953125$$

$$\approx 8.2$$

The volume is approximately 8.2 ft³.

17. Since $d = 4.5$ cm, $r = 2.25$ cm.

$$V = \frac{4}{3}\pi r^3$$

$$\approx \frac{4}{3} \cdot 3.14 \cdot 2.25^3$$

$$\approx \frac{4}{3} \cdot 3.14 \cdot 11.390625$$

$$\approx 47.689$$

The volume of one egg is approximately 47.689 cm³.
Multiply by 113.
$47.689 \cdot 113 = 5{,}389$
The total volume of the eggs is 5,389 cm³.

18. Since $d = 1$ cm, $r = 0.5$ cm.

$$V = \frac{4}{3}\pi r^3$$

$$\approx \frac{4}{3} \cdot 3.14 \cdot 0.5^3$$

$$\approx \frac{4}{3} \cdot 3.14 \cdot 0.125$$

$$\approx 0.5$$

The volume of an egg is approximately 0.5 cm³.

19. Since $d = 15$ cm, $r = 7.5$ cm.

$$V = \frac{4}{3}\pi r^3$$

$$\approx \frac{4}{3} \cdot 3.14 \cdot 7.5^3$$

$$\approx \frac{4}{3} \cdot 3.14 \cdot 421.875$$

$$\approx 1{,}766.3$$

The volume of an egg is approximately 1,766.3 cm³.

20. Since $d = 5$ in., $r = 2.5$ in.

$$V = \frac{4}{3}\pi r^3$$

$$\approx \frac{4}{3} \cdot 3.14 \cdot 2.5^3$$

$$\approx \frac{4}{3} \cdot 3.14 \cdot 15.625$$

$$\approx 65.417$$

The volume of an egg is approximately 65.417 in³.

The radius of the interior of an egg is $\left(2.5 - \frac{1}{12}\right)$ in.

Use this measurement to find the volume of the interior of the egg.

$$V = \frac{4}{3}\pi r^3$$

$$\approx \frac{4}{3} \cdot 3.14 \cdot \left(2.5 - \frac{1}{12}\right)^3$$

$$\approx \frac{4}{3} \cdot 3.14 \cdot 14.114$$

$$\approx 59.091$$

The volume of the interior of an egg is approximately 59.091 in³ · Subtract to find the volume of the shell.
$65.417 - 59.091 = 6.326$
The volume of the shell is approximately 6.3 in³.

21. Find the volume of the hemisphere by finding the volume of a sphere with radius $r$ and dividing by 2.

$$V = \frac{4}{3}\pi r^3 \div 2 = \frac{2}{3}\pi r^3$$

Find the volume of the cylinder. Note that $h = r$.
$V = \pi r^2 h = \pi r^2 \cdot r = \pi r^3$.
Add the volume of the hemisphere and the volume of the cylinder.

$$V = \frac{2}{3}\pi r^3 + \pi r^3 = \frac{5}{3}\pi r^3$$

22. $V = \frac{4}{3}\pi(2r)^3 = \frac{4}{3}\pi \, 8r^3 = 8\left(\frac{4}{3}\pi r^3\right)$

The volume is multiplied by 8.

23. Find the volume of the can. Note that the height of the can is 6 times the radius of a ball.
$V = \pi r^2 h \approx 3.14 \cdot 1.25^2 \cdot (6 \cdot 1.25) \approx 36.8 \text{ in}^3$
Find the volume of the 3 balls.

$V = 3\left(\frac{4}{3}\pi r^3\right) \approx 3 \cdot \frac{4}{3} \cdot 3.14 \cdot 1.25^3 \approx 24.5 \text{ in}^3$

Subtract: $36.8 - 24.5 = 12.3$
The volume inside the can that is not taken up by the three tennis balls is 12.3 in³.

## Focus on Higher Order Thinking

24. No; The box has a greater volume, but it would need an edge length of 8 inches, the diameter of the sphere, for the sphere to fit inside the box.

25. The cylindrical glass would hold the most water; The volume of the cylinder is $\pi r^2 \cdot r = \pi r^3$ cubic units, while the volume of the hemisphere is

$\frac{1}{2} \cdot \frac{4}{3}\pi r^3 = \frac{2}{3}\pi r^3$ cubic units and the volume of the cone is $\frac{1}{3}\pi r^2 \cdot r = \frac{1}{3}\pi r^3$ cubic units.

26. The volume of the cylinder is $\pi r^2 \cdot 2r = 2\pi r^3$ cubic units. The volume of the sphere is $\frac{4}{3}\pi r^3$ cubic units. The volume of the cone is $\frac{1}{3}\pi r^2 \cdot r = \frac{1}{3}\pi r^3$ cubic units. Therefore, the volume of the cone is one-sixth the volume of the cylinder. The volume of the sphere is two-thirds the volume of the cylinder.

27. The diameter would need to be 16 feet; The volume of the smaller balloon is

$\frac{4}{3}\pi(4)^3 = \frac{4}{3}\pi \cdot 64 \text{ ft}^3$. Since $\frac{136}{17} = 8$, the

volume of the larger balloon must be 8 times as great.

$$\frac{4}{3}\pi r^3 = 8 \cdot \frac{4}{3}\pi \cdot 64$$
$$r^3 = 8 \cdot 64$$
$$r^3 = 512$$
$$r = 8$$

Since the radius is 8 ft, the diameter is 16 ft.

## MODULE 13

### Ready to Go On?

1. $r = 6$ ft, $h = 8$ ft
$V = \pi r^2 h$
$\approx 3.14 \cdot 6^2 \cdot 8$
$\approx 3.14 \cdot 36 \cdot 8$
$\approx 904.3$
The volume is approximately 904.3 ft³.

2. $r = 4$ in., $h = 7$ in.
$V = \pi r^2 h$
$\approx 3.14 \cdot 4^2 \cdot 7$
$\approx 3.14 \cdot 16 \cdot 7$
$\approx 351.7$
The volume is approximately 351.7 in³.

3. $r = 6$ cm, $h = 15$ cm
$V = \frac{1}{3}\pi r^2 h$
$\approx \frac{1}{3} \cdot 3.14 \cdot 6^2 \cdot 15$
$\approx \frac{1}{3} \cdot 3.14 \cdot 36 \cdot 15$
$\approx 565.2$
The volume is approximately 565.2 cm³.

4. $r = 12$ in., $h = 20$ in.
$V = \frac{1}{3}\pi r^2 h$
$\approx \frac{1}{3} \cdot 3.14 \cdot 12^2 \cdot 20$
$\approx \frac{1}{3} \cdot 3.14 \cdot 144 \cdot 20$
$\approx 3,014.4$
The volume is approximately 3,014.4 in³.

5. $r = 3$ ft
$V = \frac{4}{3}\pi r^3$
$\approx \frac{4}{3} \cdot 3.14 \cdot 3^3$
$\approx \frac{4}{3} \cdot 3.14 \cdot 27$
$\approx 113$
The volume is approximately 113 ft³.

6. Since $d = 13$ cm, $r = 6.5$ cm.
$V = \frac{4}{3}\pi r^3$
$\approx \frac{4}{3} \cdot 3.14 \cdot 6.5^3$
$\approx \frac{4}{3} \cdot 3.14 \cdot 274.625$
$\approx 1,149.8$
The volume is approximately 1,149.8 cm³.

7. For a cylinder, you need to know the radius of the base and the height. For a cone, you need to know the radius of the base and the height. For a sphere, you need to know the radius.

# Solutions Key

## Statistics

**MODULE 14** *Scatter Plots*

### Are You Ready?

1. $6x - 5$ for $x = 4$
   $6(4) - 5$
   $24 - 5$
   $19$

2. $-2x + 7$ for $x = 2$
   $-2(2) + 7$
   $-4 + 7$
   $3$

3. $5x - 6$ for $x = 3$
   $5(3) - 6$
   $15 - 6$
   $9$

4. $0.5x + 8.4$ for $x = -1$
   $0.5(-1) + 8.4$
   $-0.5 + 8.4$
   $7.9$

5. $\frac{3}{4}x - 9$ for $x = -20$

   $\frac{3}{4}(-20) - 9$

   $\dfrac{3(-20^{-5})}{4_1} - 9$

   $3(-5) - 9$
   $-15 - 9$
   $-24$

6. $1.4x + 3.5$ for $x = -4$
   $1.4(-4) + 3.5$
   $-5.6 + 3.5$
   $-2.1$

7. $3x + 4 = 10$
   $\dfrac{-4 \quad -4}{3x \quad = 6}$
   $\dfrac{3x}{3} = \dfrac{6}{3}$
   $x = 2$

8. $5x - 11 = 34$
   $\dfrac{+11 \quad +11}{5x \quad = 45}$
   $\dfrac{5x}{5} = \dfrac{45}{5}$
   $x = 9$

9. $-2x + 5 = -9$
   $\dfrac{-5 \quad -5}{-2x \quad = -14}$
   $\dfrac{-2x}{-2} = \dfrac{-14}{-2}$
   $x = 7$

10. $8x + 13 = -11$
    $\dfrac{-13 \quad -13}{8x \quad = -24}$
    $\dfrac{8x}{8} = \dfrac{-24}{8}$
    $x = -3$

11. $4x - 7 = -27$
    $\dfrac{+7 \quad +7}{4x \quad = -20}$
    $\dfrac{4x}{4} = \dfrac{-20}{4}$
    $x = -5$

12. $\frac{1}{2}x + 16 = 39$
    $\dfrac{-16 \quad -16}{\frac{1}{2}x \quad = 23}$
    $2 \cdot \frac{1}{2}x = 2 \cdot 23$
    $x = 46$

13. $\frac{2}{3}x - 16 = 12$
    $\dfrac{+16 \quad +16}{\frac{2}{3}x \quad = 28}$
    $\frac{3}{2} \cdot \frac{2}{3}x = \frac{3}{2} \cdot 28$
    $x = \dfrac{3 \cdot 28^{14}}{1^{2}}$
    $x = 42$

14. $0.5x - 1.5 = -6.5$
    $\dfrac{+1.5 \quad +1.5}{0.5x \quad = -5}$
    $\dfrac{0.5x}{0.5} = \dfrac{-5}{0.5}$
    $x = -10$

### LESSON 14.1

#### Your Turn

6. The association is positive and linear. Taller students are likely to be older students and would therefore be more likely to read at a higher level.

#### Guided Practice

1.
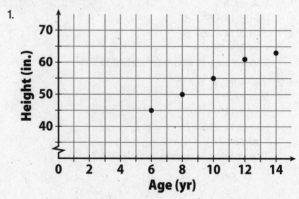

2. The association is positive and linear; As Bob gets older, his height increases. But if the data continued for increasing age, we would see that Bob's height eventually stops increasing.

3. There is a cluster in the 20–23 shots attempted range, and a lesser cluster in the 7–14 shots attempted range. The point (35, 18) is an outlier.

4. Let the numbers on the x-axis represent one variable and the numbers on the y-axis represent the other variable. Then plot points $(x, y)$ for each pair of numbers in the bivariate data set.

### Independent Practice

5. The data generally show a positive linear association. As the year increases, so does the winning distance.

6. Overall, the data from 1988 to 2012 show a negative association, even though the 8-year period from 1996 to 2004 shows a slight rise in distance jumped over time.

7. The association is nonlinear. The data points rise during the period 1960 to 1988 and then fall during the period 1988 to 2012, so there is no overall linear pattern.

8. The outlier is (1968, 8.9). This point represents a jump of 8.9 meters in 1968, a jump that far exceeds any jump made in prior or later years.

9. Sample answer: A scatter plot with no association has randomly scattered data points. There does not appear to be any pattern in the association. On a scatter plot with a negative association, the data points fall from left to right. As the values in one data set increase, the values in the other decrease.

10. Sample answer: The x-axis represents the number of people doing a job; the y-axis represents the number of hours to do the job.

11. Sample answer: The x-axis represents the number of miles a student lives from school; the y-axis represents the student's score on a 10-point quiz.

### Focus on Higher Order Thinking

12. Sample answer: You would see a number of data items with x-values and y-values that are close to one another.

13. Yes; For example, the data points may appear to lie mostly along a rising or falling curve, or may generally rise or fall, but not in a way that suggests a linear association.

14. Sample answer: Initially, the number of tickets sold might decline a little, but the price would offset the loss in sales. So, profits would increase, showing a positive association. When the price got too high, ticket sales would decline more rapidly, so profits would fall, giving a negative association.

## LESSON 14.2
### Your Turn

6. Answers may vary. Sample answer: The line passes through (0, 0) and (9, 10).
$$m = \frac{9-0}{10-0} = \frac{9}{10}, b = 0$$
The equation is $y = \frac{9}{10}x$.

### Guided Practice

1. Answers may vary. Sample answer:

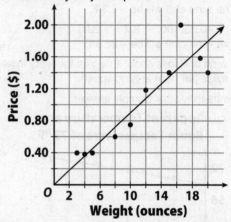

2. Most of the data points are close to the trend line and there is about the same number of points above and below the line.

3. Answers may vary slightly. Sample answer: The line passes through (0, 0) and (10, 0.80).
$$m = \frac{0.80-0}{10-0} = \frac{0.80}{10} = 0.08, b = 0$$
The equation is $y = 0.08x$.

4. $y = 0.08(7) = 0.56$
The price for 7 ounces is $0.56.
$y = 0.08(50) = 4$
The price for 50 ounces is $4.00.

5. Use the two points to write the equation of the line. Substitute in the equation the value of $x$ for which you want to make a prediction. The value of $y$ that you obtain is the prediction.

### Independent Practice

6. Answers may vary. Sample answer:

**Apparent Temperature
Due to Wind at 15 °F**

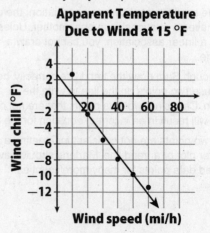

7. The trend line shows a negative linear association.

8. Answers may vary slightly. Sample answer: The line passes through $(20, -2.3)$ and $(50, -9.8)$.

$$m = \frac{-9.8 - (-2.3)}{50 - 20} = \frac{-7.5}{30} = -\frac{1}{4}, \text{ or } -0.25$$
$$y = mx + b$$
$$-2.3 = -0.25(20) + b$$
$$-2.3 = -5 + b$$
$$2.7 = b$$

The equation is $y = -0.25x + 2.7$.

9. a. $y = -0.25(36) + 2.7 = -6.3$
   The wind chill will be $-6.3°F$.

   b. $y = -0.25(100) + 2.7 = -22.3$
   The wind chill will be $-22.3°F$.

10. The wind chill falls about 1 degree for every increase of 4 miles per hour in wind speed.

11. Answers may vary. Sample answer:

**Apparent Temperature at a Room Temperature of 72 °F**

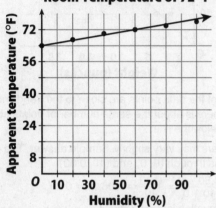

12. Answers may vary slightly. Sample answer: The line passes through $(0, 64)$ and $(60, 72)$.

$$m = \frac{72 - 64}{60 - 0} = \frac{8}{60} = \frac{2}{15}, b = 64$$

The equation is $y = \frac{2}{15}x + 64$.

13. $y = \frac{2}{15}(70) + 64 \approx 73.\overline{3}$

The apparent temperature will be about 73.3°F.

14. At 0% humidity, the apparent temperature is 64°F.

**Focus on Higher Order Thinking**

15. No; if the scatter plot shows no association, the data points have no relationship to one another. Unless there is a linear association, you cannot draw a trend line.

16. No; although Sam drew the trend line correctly, he should use two points on the line to write the equation. Choosing two data points that are not on the line will result in an incorrect equation for the line.

17. a. No; two points are not sufficient for creating a scatter plot or a trend line. Marlene should have plotted data points for many more counties.

b. Sample answer: Marlene's conjecture is incorrect. Marlene chose counties whose areas are about equal to their populations. Harris and Dallas counties provide counterexamples for Marlene's original data.

## MODULE 14

### Ready to Go On?

1.

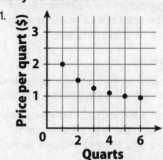

2. The association is negative but nonlinear. As the number of quarts rises, the price per quart decreases, but the data appear to lie along a curve.

3. Answers may vary. Sample answer:

**Wind Chill for 20 °F**

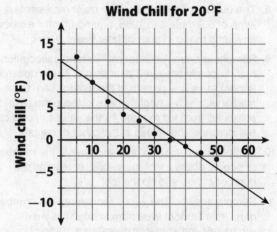

4. Answers may vary slightly. Sample answer: The line passes through $(0, 12.5)$ and $(30, 2.5)$.
$$m = \frac{2.5 - 12.5}{30 - 0} = \frac{-10}{30} = -\frac{1}{3}, b = 12.5$$
The equation is $y = -\frac{1}{3}x + 12.5$.

5. $y = -\frac{1}{3}(60) + 12.5 = -7.5$

To the nearest degree, the wind chill will be $-8°F$.

6. Sample answer: You can plot data points and draw trend lines to make predictions.

## Are You Ready?

1. $\dfrac{25}{30} = \dfrac{25 \div 5}{30 \div 5}$

$= \dfrac{5}{6}$

2. $\dfrac{27}{36} = \dfrac{27 \div 9}{36 \div 9}$

$= \dfrac{3}{4}$

3. $\dfrac{14}{16} = \dfrac{14 \div 2}{16 \div 2}$

$= \dfrac{7}{8}$

4. $\dfrac{15}{45} = \dfrac{15 \div 15}{45 \div 15}$

$= \dfrac{1}{3}$

5. $\dfrac{27}{63} = \dfrac{27 \div 9}{63 \div 9}$

$= \dfrac{3}{7}$

6. $\dfrac{45}{75} = \dfrac{45 \div 15}{75 \div 15}$

$= \dfrac{3}{5}$

7. $\dfrac{8}{27} = \dfrac{8}{27}$ because there are no common factors in the numerator and denominator other than 1.

8. $\dfrac{16}{28} = \dfrac{16 \div 4}{28 \div 4}$

$= \dfrac{4}{7}$

9.
```
   .875
8)7.000      0.875 = 87.5%
  64
  60
  56
   40
   40
    0
```

10.
```
   .8
5)4.0       0.8 = 80%
  40
   0
```

11.
```
  1.25
4)5.00      1.25 = 125%
  4
  10
   8
  20
  20
   0
```

12.
```
   .3
10)3.0       0.3 = 30%
   30
    0
```

13.
```
    .95
20)19.00      0.95 = 95%
   180
   100
   100
     0
```

14.
```
   .28
25)7.00       0.28 = 28%
   50
   200
   200
     0
```

15. 4% of 40 = 0.04 × 40

```
   40
 ×0.04
1.60 or 1.6
```

16. 7% of 300 = 0.07 × 300

```
   300
 ×0.07
21.00 or 21
```

17. 4.3% of 1,200 = 0.043 × 1,200

```
    1200
  ×0.043
    3600
   48000
51.600 or 51.6
```

18. 2.9% of 780 = 0.029 × 780

```
    780
  ×0.029
   7020
  15600
22.620 or 22.62
```

19. 1.6% of 75.20 = 0.016 × 75.20

```
    75.20
   ×0.016
    45120
   ×75200
1.20320 or 1.2032
```

20. 3.56% of 3,200 = 0.0356 × 3,200

```
     3200
   ×0.0356
    19200
   160000
   960000
113.9200 or 113.92
```

## LESSON 15.1

### Your Turn

2. Relative frequency of visiting a national park:

$$\dfrac{105}{200} = 0.525 = 52.5\%$$

Relative frequency of visiting a national park among high school students:

$\frac{80}{120} \approx 0.667 \approx 66.7\%$

Since 66.7% is greater than 52.5%, so high school students are more likely to have visited a national park than is the general population of students polled.

## Guided Practice

1. a. 50 students were surveyed.
   b. $0.6 \times 50 = 30$
      30 students have a cat.
      $50 - 30 = 20$
      20 students do not have a cat.
   c. $0.7 \times 30 = 21$
      21 students have a cat and a dog.
      $30 - 21 = 9$
      9 students have a cat and no dog.
   d. $0.75 \times 20 = 15$
      15 students have a dog and no cat.
      $20 - 15 = 5$
      5 students do not have a cat or a dog.
   e. $21 + 15 = 36$
      $9 + 5 = 14$

|        | Dog | No Dog | TOTAL |
|--------|-----|--------|-------|
| Cat    | 21  | 9      | 30    |
| No Cat | 15  | 5      | 20    |
| TOTAL  | 36  | 14     | 50    |

2. Relative frequency of being left-handed:

   $\frac{24}{240} = 0.1 = 10\%$

   Relative frequency of being a left-handed among boys:

   $\frac{14}{140} = 0.1 = 10\%$

   There is no association between being a boy and being left-handed. The relative frequency of being left-handed (10%) is the same as the relative frequency of being left-handed among boys (10%).

3. No; the poll collected data on only one variable, voters. A two-way table requires data on two variables, such as men and women.

## Independent Practice

4. Total = 140
   Take French = 111
   Do not take French = $140 - 111 = 29$
   Take French and not Spanish = 31
   Take French and Spanish = $111 - 31 = 80$
   Take neither French nor Spanish = 12
   Take Spanish and not French = $29 - 12 = 17$
   Take Spanish = $80 + 17 = 97$
   Do not take Spanish = $31 + 12 = 43$

|                        | Take French | Do NOT Take French | TOTAL |
|------------------------|-------------|--------------------|-------|
| Take Spanish           | 80          | 17                 | 97    |
| Do NOT Take Spanish    | 31          | 12                 | 43    |
| TOTAL                  | 111         | 29                 | 140   |

5. a. Eighth graders = $176 - 96 = 80$
      Seventh graders who prefer science
      $= 96 - 72 = 24$
      Total students who prefer science =
      $24 + 32 = 56$
      Total students who prefer math =
      $176 - 56 = 120$
      Eighth graders who prefer math =
      $120 - 72 = 48$

|               | Prefer Science | Prefer Math | TOTAL |
|---------------|----------------|-------------|-------|
| Seventh Grade | 24             | 72          | 96    |
| Eighth Grade  | 32             | 48          | 80    |
| TOTAL         | 56             | 120         | 176   |

   b. Relative frequency of preferring math:

      $\frac{120}{176} \approx 0.68 \approx 68\%$

      Relative frequency of preferring math among eighth graders:

      $\frac{48}{80} = 0.6 = 60\%$

      No; the relative frequency of preferring math is

      $\frac{120}{176} \approx 68\%$, and the relative frequency of preferring

      math among eighth graders is 48/80 = 60%, so eighth graders are slightly less likely to prefer math than the general population of students polled.

6. a. Total women = $98 - 33 = 65$
      Men who play woodwinds = $33 - (13 + 7 + 5)$
      $= 8$
      Women who play strings = $55 - 13 = 42$
      Women who play percussion = $9 - 5 = 4$
      Total woodwinds = $8 + 10 = 18$
      Total brass = $98 - (55 + 18 + 9) = 16$
      Women who play brass = $16 - 9 = 7$

|       | Strings | Brass | Woodwinds | Percussion | TOTAL |
|-------|---------|-------|-----------|------------|-------|
| Men   | 13      | 7     | 8         | 5          | 33    |
| Women | 42      | 9     | 10        | 4          | 65    |
| TOTAL | 55      | 16    | 18        | 9          | 98    |

   b. Yes; the relative frequency of strings players is

      $\frac{55}{98} \approx 56\%$, and the relative frequency of strings

      players among women is $\frac{42}{55} \approx 76\%$, so women

      are more likely to play strings than the general orchestra population.

## Focus on Higher Order Thinking

7. a. Relative frequency of teenagers aged 13-15 who prefer surfing:

      $\frac{52}{130} = 0.4 = 40\%$

Relative frequency of teenagers aged 13-15 who prefer snorkeling:

$$\frac{78}{130} = 0.6 = 60\%$$

Relative frequency of teenagers aged 16-18 who prefer surfing:

$$\frac{52}{80} = 0.65 = 65\%$$

Relative frequency of teenagers aged 16-18 who prefer snorkeling:

$$\frac{28}{80} = 0.35 = 35\%$$

Total percentage of students aged 16-18: 100%

Relative frequency of students who prefer surfing:

$$\frac{104}{210} \approx 0.5 \approx 50\%$$

Total percentage of students who prefer surfing: 100%

Relative frequency of students who prefer snorkeling:

$$\frac{104}{210} \approx 0.5 \approx 50\%$$

b. It is the relative frequency of teenagers who are 16 to 18 years old and who prefer snorkeling to all 16- and 18-year-olds who were surveyed.

c. Relative frequency of teenagers aged 13-15 who prefer surfing:

$$\frac{52}{104} = 0.5 = 50\%$$

Relative frequency of teenagers aged 13-15 who prefer snorkeling:

$$\frac{78}{106} \approx 0.74 \approx 74\%$$

Relative frequency of teenagers aged 16-18 who prefer surfing:

$$\frac{52}{104} = 0.5 = 50\%$$

Percentage of teenagers aged 16-18 who prefer snorkeling:

$$\frac{28}{106} \approx 0.26 \approx 26\%$$

Total percentage of students who prefer surfing: 100%

Total percentage of students who prefer snorkeling: 100%

Total percentage of students: 100%

|  | Prefer Surfing | Prefer Snorkeling | TOTAL |
|---|---|---|---|
| **Ages 13-15** | 52 40%; 50% | 78 60%; 74% | 130 100% |
| **Ages 16-18** | 52 65%; 50% | 28 35%; 26% | 80 100% |
| **TOTAL** | 104 50%; 100% | 106 50%; 100% | 210 100% |

No, the relative frequencies are not the same. The total numbers in the last column (ages) are

not the same as the total numbers in the last row (preferences), so the relative frequencies are different.

d. It is the relative frequency of teenagers who are 16 to 18 years old and who prefer snorkeling to all of those surveyed who prefer snorkeling.

## LESSON 15.2

### Your Turn

8. $\frac{0.18}{0.44} \approx 0.409 \approx 40.9\%$

9. Step 1: 44% becomes 56%
   Step 2: 45% becomes 55%; 60% becomes 40%, and 23% becomes 77%
   Step 3: The conclusions would not change.

### Guided Practice

1. a. Girl: $7 + 3 + 2 = 12$
      Boy: $5 + 2 + 6 = 13$
   b. Seashore: $7 + 5 = 12$
      Mountains: $3 + 2 = 5$
      Other: $2 + 6 = 8$
   c. Total: $12 + 13 = 25$

| Preferred Vacation / Gender | Seashore | Mountains | Other | TOTAL |
|---|---|---|---|---|
| **Girl** | 7 | 3 | 2 | 12 |
| **Boy** | 5 | 2 | 6 | 13 |
| **TOTAL** | 12 | 5 | 8 | 25 |

d. Girls who prefer seashore: $\frac{7}{25} = 0.28$

Girls who prefer mountains: $\frac{3}{25} = 0.12$

Girls who prefer other: $\frac{2}{25} = 0.08$

All girls: $\frac{12}{25} = 0.48$

Boys who prefer seashore: $\frac{5}{25} = 0.2$

Boys who prefer mountains: $\frac{2}{25} = 0.08$

Boys who prefer other: $\frac{6}{25} = 0.24$

All boys: $\frac{13}{25} = 0.52$

All students who prefer seashore: $\frac{12}{25} = 0.48$

All students who prefer mountains: $\frac{5}{25} = 0.2$

All students who prefer other: $\frac{8}{25} = 0.32$

All students: $\frac{25}{25} = 1.00$

| Preferred Vacation / Gender | Seashore | Mountains | Other | TOTAL |
|---|---|---|---|---|
| Girl | 0.28 | 0.12 | 0.08 | 0.48 |
| Boy | 0.2 | 0.08 | 0.24 | 0.52 |
| TOTAL | 0.48 | 0.2 | 0.32 | 1.00 |

e. 0.08, or 8%

f. 0.48, or 48%

g. $\frac{1}{4} = 0.25 = 25\%$

Girls are more likely than boys to prefer the mountains.

2. You can find joint relative frequencies, marginal relative frequencies, conditional relative frequencies, and possible associations.

## Independent Practice

3. a. No job total: $75 - 51 = 24$
   Job and clubs only: $15 - 5 = 10$
   No job and sports only: $18 - 12 = 6$
   Job and both clubs and sports:
   $51 - (10 + 12 + 9) = 20$
   Total for jobs and both clubs and sports:
   $20 + 10 = 30$
   No job and neither: $24 - (5 + 6 + 10) = 3$
   Total for neither clubs or sports: $9 + 3 = 12$

| Activity/ Job | Clubs Only | Sports Only | Both | Neither | TOTAL |
|---|---|---|---|---|---|
| Yes | 10 | 12 | 20 | 9 | 51 |
| No | 5 | 6 | 10 | 3 | 24 |
| TOTAL | 15 | 18 | 30 | 12 | 75 |

b. Sample answer: I worked backward from the given data, using the fact that sum of the entries in each row and column must equal the total for that row or column.

4. Job and clubs only: $\frac{10}{75} \approx 0.13$

Job and sports only: $\frac{12}{75} = 0.16$

Job and both clubs and sports: $\frac{20}{75} \approx 0.27$

Job and neither clubs nor sports: $\frac{9}{75} = 0.12$

Job total: $\frac{51}{75} = 0.68$

No jobs and clubs only: $\frac{5}{75} \approx 0.07$

No jobs and sports only: $\frac{6}{75} = 0.08$

No job and both clubs and sports: $\frac{10}{75} \approx 0.13$

No job and neither clubs nor sports: $\frac{3}{75} = 0.04$

No job total: $\frac{24}{75} = 0.32$

Clubs only total: $\frac{15}{75} = 0.2$

Sports only total: $\frac{18}{75} = 0.24$

Both clubs and sports total: $\frac{30}{75} = 0.4$

Neither clubs nor sports total: $\frac{12}{75} = 0.16$

Total: $\frac{75}{75} = 1.00$

| Activity/ Job | Clubs Only | Sports Only | Both | Neither | TOTAL |
|---|---|---|---|---|---|
| Yes | 0.13 | 0.16 | 0.27 | 0.12 | 0.68 |
| No | 0.07 | 0.08 | 0.13 | 0.04 | 0.32 |
| TOTAL | 0.2 | 0.24 | 0.4 | 0.16 | 1.00 |

5. a. $0.13 = 13\%$
   b. $0.32 = 32\%$
   c. $\frac{20}{51} \approx 0.39 \approx 39\%$

6. Job with clubs only: $\frac{10}{15} \approx 0.67 \approx 67\%$

Job with sports only: $\frac{12}{18} \approx 0.67 \approx 67\%$

Job with both clubs and sports: $\frac{20}{30} \approx 0.67 \approx 67\%$

$\frac{9}{12} = 0.75 = 75\%$

Sample answer: There does not appear to be any influence. Within each category of school activity, the percent of students who have a part-time job is fairly close to 68%, the percent for the whole group.

## Focus on Higher Order Thinking

7. a. No; each data value should have been divided by the grand total, 600, not by the row total.
   b. White oak accepted:
   $\frac{245}{350} \approx 0.82, \frac{245}{600} \approx 0.41$

   White oak rejected: $\frac{105}{350} = 0.3, \frac{245}{600} \approx 0.18$

   White oak total: $\frac{350}{350} = 1.00, \frac{350}{600} \approx 0.58$

   Redwood accepted: $\frac{140}{250} = 0.56, \frac{140}{600} \approx 0.23$

   Redwood rejected: $\frac{110}{250} = 0.44, \frac{110}{600} \approx 0.18$

   Redwood total: $\frac{250}{250} = 1.00, \frac{250}{600} \approx 0.42$

   Accepted total: $\frac{385}{600} \approx 0.64$

   Rejected total: $\frac{215}{600} \approx 0.36$

   Total: $\frac{600}{600} = 1.00$

   Yes; the data in the Total row and Total column are correct. These entries are created by dividing each entry by 600, the grand total, which results in the correct marginal relative frequency. The joint relative frequencies are incorrect.

8. Relative frequency is the quotient of a frequency and the grand total. Conditional relative frequency is the quotient of a frequency and a column total or row total.

## MODULE 15

### Ready to Go On?

1. 90

2. $110 - 70 = 40$

3. $\frac{90}{200} = 0.45 = 45\%$

4. $\frac{42}{112} = 0.375$

5. 0.12

6. 0.42

7. $\frac{0.14}{0.42} \approx 0.33$

8. You can use two-way tables to find frequencies, various types of relative frequencies, and possible associations.